THROUGH GEOLOGIC TIME

W9-BIZ-288

Mesozoic meso (middle), zoe (life)		Paleozoic paleo (old), zoe (life)	continued on back endpapers
Cycad JURASSIC 135–180 Allosaurus	Saltoposuchus TRIASSIC 180–220 Cynognathus	Dimetrodon PERMIAN 220–275 Acanthodes	Giant Lycopod UPPER CARBONIFEROUS (Pennsylvanian) 275–330 Cornuboniscus
Nevadian disturbance deformed West Coast of North America; Sierra Nevadas formed.	Palisades disturbance caused volcanic activity along East Coast of North America.	Appalachians south of New England formed; Ouachitas further disturbed by the Appalachian disturbance. Ural Mountains formed and Variscans further deformed. Volcanic activity along the West Coast of North America.	Main deformation of the Ouachita Mountains of Oklahoma and Arkansas.
Extensive spreading of seas over large areas of Asia, Europe, parts of California and Oregon. No evidence of icecaps during this period. Great southern continent "Gondwanaland" began to divide.		Western U.S. covered by seas. In other parts of Northern Hemisphere seas dried up leaving vast deposits of salt and potash. Glaciers covered equatorial regions—India, Africa, Australia, South America.	Uplifting of sea beds in Northern Hemisphere produced new low-lying land. Other areas sank, giving rise to vast lakes and brackish lagoons.
Varied and abundant, although true flowering plants had not yet appeared.	In the Northern Hemisphere at the end of this period conifers, cycads, and ferns became widespread and persisted for for the next 100 million years.	Conifers began to increase. The giant horsetails and other early trees began to die out.	About half of the world's workable coal was formed during this period.
Ammonites were widespread. Crabs and flies appeared for the first time. Reptiles dominated the land. One stock of reptiles evolved into the first birds.	Mammals evolved from the reptiles. First appearance of dinosaurs and lobsterlike crustaceans.	Some corals, the trilobites, and other animal groups became extinct. Wide variety of reptiles, including reptiles from which mammals are believed to have evolved.	Many winged insects, one with wing span of 29 inches. Salamanderlike amphibians 15 feet long. Earliest known reptiles.

contents

a planet is born

How old is our planet? Is it still in its youth, or is it now entering old age? Does, in fact, a planet "grow old?" If so, how? Is the earth shrinking, or is it getting larger? What mysterious forces are at work deep inside our restless globe—forces that make the earth an ever-changing planet? For example, some scientists think that between one million and sixty million years ago the earth's north and south magnetic poles reversed places many times. If this happened, how do these scientists account for "reversing" poles? What tremendous upheavals in the earth's past upturned mountains and left a great circle of volcanoes dotting the rim of the Pacific Ocean basin? Are we now facing another ice age in which a vast glacier will eventually creep down and cover much of North America and Europe?

In the past one hundred years or so man has left hardly a square mile of surface land and surface sea unexplored. He has mapped the steaming jungles of the tropics and the gleaming ice fields of the poles. And even now he is taking his first cautious steps into space. Yet just beneath our feet, beneath the eggshell-thin crust of our planet, lie vast unexplored regions of the earth—regions we will never see and may never fully understand. The mean distance to the center of the earth is 3,959 miles. The dream of some scientists is to drill a hole as deep as that and draw up a continuous sample of earth-matter, a sample reaching from our planet's surface to its very core. To date, the deepest hole man

5

Early in its history the earth was a barren planet of rock. Great outpourings of lava flowed over many parts of its surface. Later, centuries of rain eroded the rocks and filled depressions which became the first seas; from the seas life then began its triumphant march.

In 1755, Kant said that the Sun and planets were formed from a cloud of dust and gas. Particles in the cloud collected into globes, contracted, and grew hot. Millions of years later the planet-globes cooled.

has drilled into the earth is about five miles—a mere one-thousandth of the way to the earth's center. But as this book is being written a team of scientists is selecting a spot on the floor of the Atlantic where they hope to drill a hole through the earth's crust to the mantle. The hole will be about six and a half miles deep.

Unlike geologists, who can examine rock samples lying about on the ground, scientists interested in the earth's interior, face a more diffi-cult problem. But this does not mean that they know nothing of the earth's interior. By studying the speed and direction of earthquake waves, which are constantly tremoring through our planet, and by analyzing lava flows from volcanoes, scientists can tell us much about the earth's inside. Such is the job of geophysicists—to explore the dark, invisible three-quarters of the earth. With each new fragment of knowledge these scientists are able to give us, we come to understand our earth-home a little more.

Before we probe into the earth and try to understand the mysterious forces that produce volcanoes and earthquakes, that have raised moun-tains, and that make the earth a giant magnet, we might first ask: "How was our planet born?" But isn't this the astronomer's concern? you may wonder. It is, of course, but the geophysicist and geochemist also have an interest in this question. If they understood just how our planet was formed, their job of determining the structure and composition of our globe would be easier.

6

the earth from dust

Every major theory explaining how the planets may have been formed falls within two general ideas: 1. the planets were formed directly from a star; or 2. along with the sun they were formed out of a vast cloud of dust and gas.

In 1755 the German philosopher, Immanuel Kant, said that the sun and its family of planets were formed out of an immense cloud of dust and gas. Certain forces within the cloud, said Kant, set it spinning like a cosmic phonograph record. Over many years the individual dust and gas particles collected into great globes. As the material forming these globes packed itself tighter and tighter around the central core, the globes became hot spheres. Millions of years later the spheres cooled and developed into the planets as we know them today. In a sense it's remarkable that this early theory of the planets' origin is not too different from a leading modern theory.

Twenty-three years after Kant published his solar system theory a French naturalist, Comte de Buffon, offered a rather different account of the planets' birth. In Buffon's account our region of space at one time was occupied only by the sun which was without a family of planets. But, said Buffon, one day a "comet" [he most likely meant a star] crashed into the sun. The result: Huge globes of matter splashed out around the sun, cooled, solidified, and became the planets.

In 1778, Comte de Buffon said that a "comet" plunged into the Sun, splattering huge globes of matter out into space. Eventually the gaseous globes cooled, acquired hard surfaces, and became the Sun's planets.

Thinking along the same lines as Kant, a French astronomer named Pierre Simon de Laplace announced his "ring" theory in 1796. Like Kant, Laplace began with a great cloud of dust and gas. As the cloud radiated heat off into space, Laplace said, it began closing in on itself. And as it contracted it started to spin and flatten out into a giant disk. After many years, when the spinning reached a certain speed, the disk threw off a great ring of gas and dust. Many years later another ring was cast off, and another, and another. Gradually, said Laplace, each ring collected into a globe, cooled, and became a planet. The globe of gas and dust remaining at the disk's center became the sun.

In 1900, F. R. Moulton and T. C. Chamberlin, two American scientists, used Buffon's solar stage for their planetary drama. According to their "planetesimal" theory, a foreign star X once passed dangerously close to the sun, possibly within three million miles. During the approach and passing, two gigantic tidal bulges were raised on the sun. The closer star X came to the sun, the greater grew the tides. Finally, at the moment of passing, the top part of each tidal bulge on the sun was torn free and thrown out into surrounding space. After star X had passed, some of the debris was drawn back into the sun, but most of it remained as a great flat ring circling the sun. Gradually the ring material solidified into thousands of small chunks called "planetesimals." Over many years the large planetesimals swept up the smaller ones and so became the planets with their moons.

An interesting side light of this theory, sometimes overlooked, is that what happened to the sun also happened to star X. Namely, star X carried away with it an infant planetary system of its own. As we'll discover in a few pages, the idea of planetesimals is a most attractive one, regardless of how they came into being.

Eighteen years after Moulton and Chamberlin introduced their theory, the two British astronomers, Sir James Jeans and Harold Jeffreys, published their "tidal" theory. This was not unlike the Moulton-Chamberlin idea. One difference is that instead of being a near miss, star X grazed the sun as it swept past. The second difference is that just after the grazing a cigar-shaped filament of gas, rather than a disk, was formed. Gradually the material in the thicker section of the cigar solidified into globes which became the giant planets. The material at the thin ends of the cigar condensed and became the smaller planets.

8

From Kant to Jeans and Jeffreys, each attempt to explain how the planets were born fails the test of modern astronomy. Each theory mentioned so far, astronomers feel, has certain weaknesses that make it unacceptable. Within the past ten years or so, however, two new theories have been offered—one by a British astronomer and the other by a German physicist. The British astronomer Fred Hoyle tells us that the sun once may have had a companion star which exploded. Some of its matter was hurled far out into space; some of it was drawn into the sun; and some of it settled in a great ring circling the sun. The ring matter, Hoyle says, eventually collected into giant globes many times larger than the planets today. As they continued to sweep up solar debris they became larger and larger, and finally they began to break apart. The larger chunks became the major planets and the smaller ones became the minor planets. And even smaller ones became satellite prisoners, or moons, of the planets.

Many astronomers and physicists see great promise in the theory developed by the German astrophysicist Carl von Weizsäcker and revised by Gerard Kuiper, George Gamow, and others. The Weizsäcker picture shows us a cloudy infant sun at the center of a vast, spinning cloud of dust and gas not unlike Kant's dust cloud. Gradually hundreds of huge whirlpools formed within the disk. Where the whirlpools' edges brushed against each other, small "roller-bearing" globes of dust and gas collected. Slowly these globes condensed into the planets, in the process developing their own gas-and-dust rings from which their moons were formed.

As promising as Weizsäcker's idea appears to astronomers, it leaves many questions unanswered—questions which only time and more research may be able to settle. One criticism of Kuiper's, for instance, is that the planets could not have formed directly out of the small roller-bearing globes. He feels that the globes could not have lasted for more than ten to a hundred years—too short a time for planet formation. Kuiper does think, however, that the larger whirlpool globes were large enough, and lasted long enough, for the planets to form directly from them.

Whether or not the Weizsäcker theory will pass the test of time is anyone's guess now. There is a possibility, disturbing perhaps to many of us, that man will *never* know for certain how the earth came into being. If no single theory answers our question, then we can ask a broader question: "Were the planets born 'hot' or 'cool'?" If the answer is "hot," then they developed directly from a star. But if the answer is "cool," then they must have developed from a gas-and-dust cloud that slowly contracted and in the process became hot.

The deeper we dig into the earth, the higher the temperature becomes. At the bottom of California's deepest oil wells the temperature is above the boiling point of water. For example, a western Texas well 25,340 feet deep has a static bottom temperature of 380°F. Glowing lavas that flow from volcanoes also tell us that there is great heat within the earth. But has this heat always been there—from the earth's beginning? The only way the nineteenth-century British physicist, Lord Kelvin, could account for the heat of volcanoes was to suppose that our planet was formed hot, from a great molten globe that has been cooling ever since. For many years Kelvin's "hot planet" idea was accepted by most authorities. But recently scientists have come to favor the opposite point of view: that the earth was formed "cool" and is now warming up.

Harold C. Urey tells us that most likely the earth was formed by larger chunks of matter sweeping up smaller ones after the great dust ring circling the sun began developing solid particles. If this sweeping-up process had taken place in a short time—less than about five million years—the young earth probably would have melted as it was forming. There would have been at least two heat sources—one resulting from cosmic debris plunging into the young earth and so adding to its mass, another resulting from radioactivity. On the other hand, if the sweeping-up process had taken a longer time the young earth would have formed at lower temperatures, possibly near 1000°C. In any case, Urey feels that the earth did heat up as it continued forming, and that its rate of heating then was much greater than it is now. One reason could have been that during the earth's molten stage large amounts of iron in outer regions of the planet began flowing through channels into the core. This mass migration of iron would have generated much heat. Urey reasons that to account for the present molten iron core of the earth about fifty thousand tons of iron must have flowed into the core *every second* for a period of five hundred million years. Other estimates put a slower iron flow at a duration of two billion years. In either case, Urey says, "If this reasoning is correct, the earth was made initially with some iron in its exterior parts, and at one time it could have been completely molten."

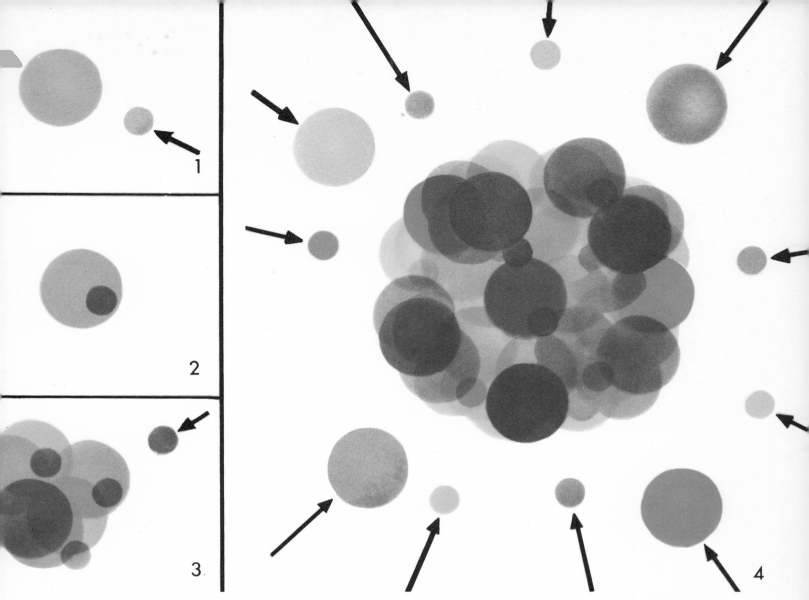

The earth may have been formed as larger chunks of matter swept up smaller ones after the great dust ring circling the Sun developed solid particles. The larger the aggregation, the greater its attracting force.

In its initial cool stage, then, the earth may have accumulated from a variety of gases and dust, then later from chunks of ammonia-snow and water-snow. Gradually, as the infant planet swept up more and more matter, it grew warm, then hot as the matter packed itself tighter and tighter around the central core and so generated heat. During the heating stage many chemical reactions were taking place. Compounds of carbon, nitrogen, oxygen, and hydrogen were being built up and broken down. Silicates, which later formed part of the earth's crust, were melting. And iron oxides were being reduced to iron. Eventually the young earth became a molten globe. It was during this stage that iron melted and flowed down through the mushy silicates into the core, displacing lighter rocky material which rose toward the surface. Gradually the planet cooled enough so that eventually it developed the crust we walk on today.

11

formation of the atmosphere

Among the many puzzles associated with our planet are how the atmosphere was formed and what was its original make-up. Today we know that the earth's blanket of air is made up roughly of four-fifths nitrogen, one-fifth oxygen and small amounts of water vapor, carbon dioxide, ozone, and several other gases. Geochemists are certain that the mixture of gases about us today has not always enveloped our planet. Just how and when our present air mixture developed, however, are not easily explained, because we still do not know exactly how the earth itself was formed. If scientists knew this, they would be on safer ground when they try to account for the earth's primitive and present atmospheres.

Gerard Kuiper, Urey, and other scientists have tried to reconstruct the chain of events that many millions of years ago may have provided the beginning to the atmosphere story. Again our starting point is the infant earth, a loosely packed globe sweeping up gas, dust, ammonia-snow, and water-snow as it circled the young sun. At this stage in the earth's history it had a primitive atmosphere, but entirely different from the one we know today. By weight it was made up of ninety-seven per cent free hydrogen and helium with small amounts of neon, water vapor, ammonia, methane (marsh gas), and argon. Gradually, however, the young earth began to lose its atmosphere. Light rays from a young blazing sun began "blowing away" the lightweight gases—hydrogen, helium, and neon. Over a period of a hundred million years or so most of the primitive atmosphere escaped into space, leaving the heavier gases of water vapor, ammonia, and methane to the last.

But even as the sun's radiation was driving away the earth's original gases, our planet began developing a new atmosphere. Ultraviolet energy from the sun was breaking down the water vapor, ammonia, and methane, splitting their molecules. From the water vapor (H_2O) oxygen was released and remained free in the new-forming atmosphere, but the freed hydrogen leaked away into space. Some of the oxygen attacked ammonia molecules (NH_3), producing free nitrogen and water vapor. Oxygen also attacked methane molecules (CH_4), changing them into carbon dioxide and more water vapor. So at this stage free oxygen, nitrogen, carbon dioxide, and water vapor (all present in our atmosphere today) were being formed by light energy from the sun. But something else was

12

happening to our young planet, something that was adding still more gases to its new atmosphere.

As the earth-matter was packing itself more and more tightly around the core it was generating heat by compression and by radioactivity. So a variety of chemical reactions were taking place inside the earth. Over millions of years the heating earth released great quantities of steam, water, carbon dioxide, carbon monoxide, nitrogen, and other gases. They bubbled, belched, and hissed from molten pools and openings in the soft primitive crust. Where the surface was extremely hot, outpourings of water were vaporized and broken down into free oxygen and hydrogen with the hydrogen always escaping into space. The steam rose into the upper air where its water vapor was chemically divided into free oxygen and hydrogen. Eventually the age of volcanoes dawned. Great outpourings released carbon dioxide, carbon monoxide, and nitrogen into the air. Today's atmospheric nitrogen, according to Kuiper, is probably mostly volcanic in origin, since the earth's mantle contains fifty times more nitrogen than the present air itself.

Untold millions of years after the new atmosphere began forming, the great chain of life began. Simple plants, then more complex ones, appeared and added more oxygen to the air through photosynthesis. The make-up of the air today is most likely very nearly the same as it was half a billion years ago, yet even now it is changing. Volcanic exhalations and man's factories are constantly pouring gases into the air. The weathering of rocks releases gases as does the atmosphere's interaction with the oceans. And even today radiation from the sun is constantly breaking down and building up gas molecules in the upper regions of the atmosphere. The change is never-ending. Yet the balance of gases in the air has changed very little since man appeared on this planet. As we'll discover in the following chapters, the process of change within the earth is slow, unbelievably slow, as measured by human time.

BIRTH OF THE OCEANS

The origin of the oceans, like the origin of the earth itself, may forever remain a mystery. Scientists can reconstruct only what they suppose may have happened in the earth's dim past to produce the water that now covers 70.8 per cent of the earth's surface.

At least two billion years ago the hot earth cooled enough to develop a crust. The mushy lightweight rocky materials that rose to the surface of the earlier molten globe had cooled and "froze" into solid material at 1000° to 2000°.

During this epoch great gushers of steam, nitrogen and other gases hissed into the atmosphere. As the water vapor rose to cold regions of the upper air it condensed into rain and fell toward earth. But the great masses of rocks were not yet cool enough for the rain to settle on them. As torrents of water poured down on the earth they were instantly heated and changed back into steam and driven in great turbulent clouds high into the atmosphere again.

At this time in the earth's history, and for several million years, vast dark storm clouds must have raged over our planet, preventing any sunlight from reaching the surface. But gradually, as the rocks cooled, the rains fell, forming angry swirling rivers that pounded over rocky plains and etched their way down mountains.

By this time huge flows of underground water were welling up to the surface. For hundreds of years the rains continued to fall and flow into shallow depressions and great trenches, gradually filling the ocean basins. As the primeval rivers and streams washed down toward the seas, they picked up, dissolved and carried salts with them.

Over the years, as ocean water evaporated and fell again as rain, the salts remained behind, accumulating in the seas, as they are still accumulating today.

Eventually, after how many dark centuries we don't know, the great rains eased and finally stopped. Dim light began penetrating the thinning clouds and one day the sun's rays broke through for the first time, illuminating a new planet of jagged rock and blue water. ⟶

geology becomes a science

shape and size of the earth

Today we know that the earth is a sphere slightly flattened at the poles, or an "oblate spheroid." And we know that if we leave, say, New York and continue traveling in a straight easterly direction, we will eventually return to our starting point. But men have not always known these facts. For many years they believed the earth was shaped like a great drum. Nor have they known for very long just how large the earth is. Some of the early Greek philosopher-scientists thought that the earth extended only a small distance around the Mediterranean Sea: from northern Africa in the south to a range of high mountains in the north, and from the "world ocean" in the west to parts of Asia in the east. After all, why shouldn't they have thought this? Without swift transportation, or means of long-range communication, their ability to explore the earth and learn about its surface by direct observation was severely limited. Quite likely primitive peoples the world over, long before the Greek philosophers, also thought that the earth did not extend far beyond the areas they inhabited.

One of the first Greek philosophers we know about was named Thales, who lived during the seventh century B.C. Writings about him tell us that he believed all things were made of *water*. How Thales came to believe this we don't know. Spring water and wells bubbling out of the ground perhaps led him to think that the earth rested on water. And he could see mist rising from the ground, evaporating, then falling to earth as rain water. About a hundred years following Thales we find another philosopher, Xenophanes, saying that the earth's limit "above is seen at our feet in contact with the air; below it reaches down without a limit." He also thought that the earth extended horizontally forever, or to infinity. Around 500 B.C. Anaxagoras taught that the earth is "flat in shape and remains suspended because of its size and because there is no vacuum." The air surrounding the earth, he thought, held it up in space. He also said that the earth is hollow and that the sea and rivers flow out of great cavities within the earth. Earthquakes, he believed, were caused by air above the earth rushing against air beneath it.

In 384 B.C. Aristotle, who became one of the greatest teachers of all time, was born. In addition to reviewing earlier men's ideas about the shape and size of the earth Aristotle set forth ideas of his own, ideas that future scholars were to cling to for nearly two thousand years. Most of the great thinkers of Aristotle's day believed that the earth was flat. But the philosopher tried to prove to them that this could not be so. The

For many years men thought that the earth was shaped like a great drum or disk. Some of the early Greek philosophers thought that the earth extended only a small distance around the Mediterranean. Today we know that the earth is an oblate spheroid, a bit flat at the poles (the equatorial diameter being twenty-six miles greater than the distance from pole to pole). Recent satellite research has shown us that our planet is slightly pear-shaped (much exaggerated in diagram).

Curvature of the earth is revealed as an observer sees a ship disappear over the horizon. Insert shows the shore observer's view of the ship as it would appear on the horizon along his line of sight (see diagram).

earth must be a sphere, he said. You can see this for yourself, he told the doubters, if you watch a ship sail over the horizon. First the body of the ship drops slowly out of sight, then the mast disappears bit by bit. Does this not prove that the oceans are curved, not flat? And during an eclipse, he said, the earth's shadow cast on the moon shows that the earth is curved, not flat. As sound as these arguments were, they convinced few scholars of Aristotle's time. It was more comfortable to go along with the old "established" beliefs. Many people who heard Aristotle could not understand why, if the earth were round, people on the under side did not "fall off," or how they managed to walk "upside down." Newton's laws of gravitation, which could explain these things, were two thousand years in the future. Aristotle's critics thought that "up" and "down" were absolute directions in space. They could not understand that "up" would become "down" if they traveled to the opposite side of the earth.

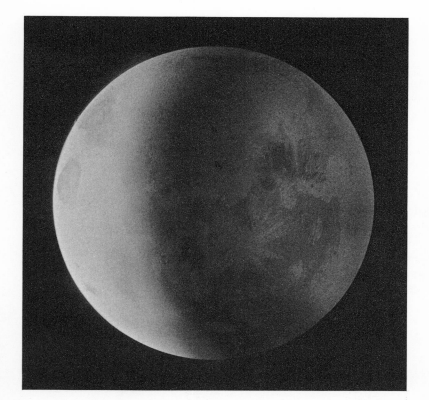

Aristotle said that the earth's curved shadow, cast on the moon during an eclipse, showed that the earth is curved, not flat.

Aristotle also attacked earlier ideas maintaining that within the earth are water-filled cavities from which rivers and the seas flow. Rivers, Aristotle told his students, are formed in the mountains and eventually flow into the sea. He taught, too, that "mainland and sea exchange places and one area does not always remain earth, another sea, for all time, but where there is now sea there is at another time land." This accurate observation later became a major thought in the work of the nineteenth-century geologist Sir Charles Lyell.

On earthquakes, according to Harvard's L. Don Leet, Aristotle "launched a thousand ships of fantasy. . . . He constructed a series of philosophical gems and scientific absurdities." The cause of earthquakes, Aristotle told his listeners, was winds which blew into caverns within the earth and became imprisoned. When their pressure within the caverns built up to the straining point they escaped forcefully and caused the earth to tremble. Earlier, Democritus supposed that the earth's hollows collected water, and when an excess of water sloshed from one place to another within the earth the earth trembled. The true causes of earthquakes were a long time being revealed; in fact, although we understand much more about them than Aristotle did, the causes of earthquakes are by no means fully understood even today.

Although Aristotle proved that the earth is a sphere, no one before him or during his lifetime managed to measure the size of our planet accurately. But how could a man accomplish this feat without taking a trip around the earth? The answer came from a brilliant librarian named Eratosthenes in the third century B.C. Eratosthenes lived in Alexandria, which was five hundred miles away from a settlement known as Syene. One day a friend told him that in Syene on a certain day of the year (at equinox) the noon sun shone straight down so that vertical objects did not cast a shadow. But on the same day in Alexandria this did not happen. Eratosthenes knew that during equinox in Alexandria the sun passed seven degrees from the direct overhead position or "zenith." The librarian reasoned that if the earth's surface were curved the sun would, of course, strike the two cities at two different angles, as shown in the diagram. He also reasoned that the angle formed by the sun's rays striking a vertical rod in Alexandria would be the same as the angle formed by lines drawn from the earth's center to each of the cities—seven degrees, or about one-fiftieth of the full circle. The final step was for

19

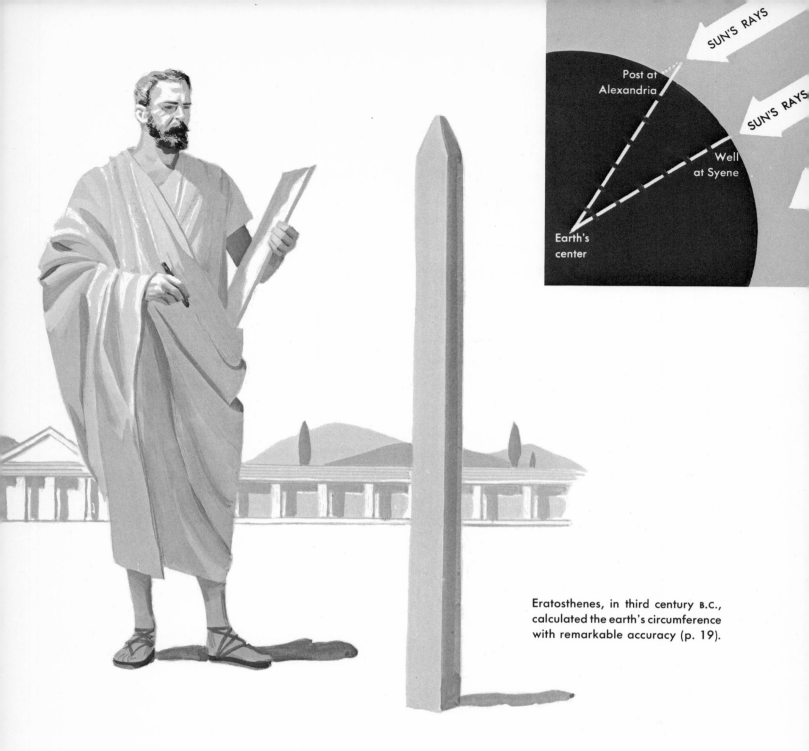

Eratosthenes, in third century B.C., calculated the earth's circumference with remarkable accuracy (p. 19).

Eratosthenes to multiply fifty by five hundred (the distance between the two cities). The result in miles, 25,000, he said, must be the circumference, or distance around the earth. (Eratosthenes did not use miles as his unit of measure, but *stadia*, which are equal to one-tenth of a mile.) This was a remarkable calculation for the time; the librarian was off by only 130 miles or so, the circumference of the earth being about 24,874 miles. But even more remarkable was the discovery that the earth was so large! Some of Eratosthenes' friends must have found it hard to believe that the area of the earth was several hundred times larger than the then-known land masses.

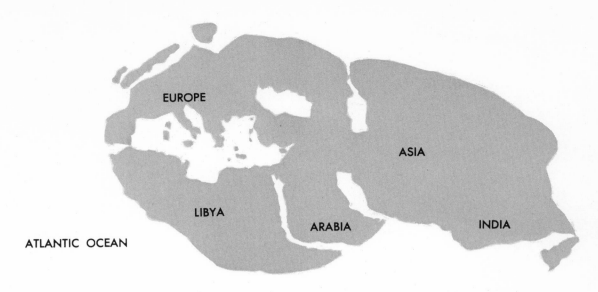

EUROPE

ASIA

LIBYA

ARABIA

INDIA

ATLANTIC OCEAN

Assuming that the world was a sphere, Eratosthenes said a ship sailing west from Spain would reach India.

digging for new facts

Not until the 1600's and 1700's do we find promising advances being made in geology. For nearly two thousand years the ideas of Aristotle—the sound and unsound alike—were taught and stubbornly defended by scholars. The breakaway into the age of scientific enlightenment was a slow and sometimes painful process. Slow because a careful examination of large land areas by one man is time-consuming; and painful because many of the early geologists lived to see their life's work crumble under the pressure of new facts.

In 1681 Thomas Burnet, a clergyman at Cambridge University, tried to explain the earth's surface features by following the biblical account of the Flood. Burnet reasoned that the earth was once a smooth-skinned planet partly filled with water. After many years of being heated by the sun the earth's crust cracked and broke open. Enormous blocks of earth plunged into the subterranean ocean, forcing water in gigantic waves to surge and pound overland, devastating all it touched. Mountains were raised and deep valleys were gouged. Great chunks of earth were folded, tumbled, and twisted this way and that. In Burnet's thinking the biblical Flood is so accounted for, a flood that left the earth a shattered and chaotic globe. Although scholars and clergymen attacked Burnet's theory, many went along with him, part of the way at least. They said that the Flood must have raised the earth's mountains. If not, they argued, how do we account for sea shells entombed in mountain rock? Surely these are remains of creatures washed high by the Flood. Many years were to pass before this problem found a solution.

21

On entering mine shafts in his native Germany, Abraham Werner saw that the walls of earth were divided in layers, or *strata*. He thought such layers existed the world over and were laid down by great floods.

The "world ocean" or "flood" ideas struck many geologists as a sound starting point to explain the surface features of the land. Among them was the German geologist Abraham Gottlob Werner, born in 1750. On descending mine shafts in his native Saxony, Werner saw that the walls of earth were divided in layers, or *strata* as in a layer cake. Werner was not a traveler, so he assumed that the same kind of strata must exist the world over, and that they were formed one atop another in the same order in China as in Saxony. His problem was to explain how the strata were formed. It seemed logical to suppose that a vast ocean flooded the world and then dried up, time and time again in the earth's history. Each time there was a flood, Werner reasoned, a new layer of earth and mountains would be formed. He saw the earth composed of layers like an onion, each layer formed in a given flood period of geologic time. Because Werner looked to a world ocean to explain strata in the crust, his followers were called Neptunists, from the Roman god of the sea, Neptune.

If Werner were correct, then all the rocks he observed should have been *sedimentary* rocks—that is, rocks formed from earthy deposits that settled out from the seas. But Werner saw a different kind of rock, which his theory could not account for. Called *basalt,* these rocks are dark gray to black in color and are fine-grained. The French geologist Nicolas Desmarest, born in 1725, took a particular interest in these rocks as he saw them strewn about areas of Auvergne. He felt sure that these rocks, now called *igneous* from the Latin word for "fire," were not formed by ocean sediments; they must be volcanic in origin.

22

When Desmarest learned that there were many old volcanoes scattered over his section of the globe he came to this conclusion: In remote time the active volcanoes emitted great quantities of lava which seeped and flowed up through cracks and fissures in the surface sedimentary rock. On solidifying, the lava became basalt. Many of Desmarest's followers relied too strongly on volcanoes to account for the earth's formation. As a result these men were called Vulcanists, after the Roman god of fire, Vulcan.

In 1795 the Scottish physician-farmer-chemist-geologist James Hutton published a book entitled *Theory of the Earth*. In it Hutton wrote that the earth has "no vestige of a beginning, no prospect of an end." He saw a world of eternal change brought about by natural forces—great upheavals within the earth producing changes on the surface, and rain, wind, and rivers constantly sculpturing the earth's face. Hutton maintained, and correctly so, that great heat within the earth could melt solid objects. He also said that this heat long ago caused many mountains to rise up higher than the seas. Such action would account for igneous rocks. Sedimentary rocks, he said, are formed over many years as rain and rivers wash sediments toward the sea. Amid many objections Hutton maintained that igneous basalt is produced by high heat and pressure acting on lava. He also held that heat and pressure changes the sedimentary rock limestone into marble. In short, Hutton's "Plutonism" (named after the Greek god of the underworld, Pluto) explained all rocks found the world over.

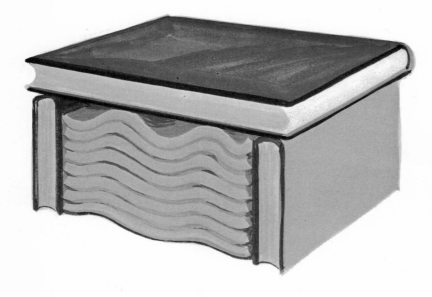

24

Lyell said that wrinkling and folding of strata making up our planet's crust had been going on throughout geologic time. He demonstrated warped strata by squeezing a stack of papers between upright books.

Critics of Hutton, mainly the Neptunists, claimed that basalt could not come from lava. On cooling, they said, molten lava turns brittle and not crystalline. And when limestone was heated, they maintained, it turned to quicklime, not marble. On these points a Scottish friend of Hutton's, Sir James Hall, born in 1761, came to the rescue. By packing limestone into a gun barrel and heating it under pressure, Hall managed to change the limestone to marble, not quicklime. And he discovered that lava when melted and cooled could be turned into either a smooth, black glass-like substance *or* into a basalt-like rock. Slow or rapid cooling determined what would happen to the lava. Cooled slowly it became basalt. Here, then, was positive proof that Hutton was correct.

In 1830 the English geologist Sir Charles Lyell published his *Principles of Geology.* In the three-volume work Lyell reviewed all the important studies made to date. The old myths of geology were severely attacked by Lyell. He ridiculed the idea that floods had moved mountains and sculptured the landscape. Lyell said that "the land has never in a single instance gone down suddenly for several hundred feet at once. . . . Great but slow oscillations brought dry land several thousand feet below sea level and raised it thousands of feet above." Lyell also held to the idea of eternal change. Even today, he said, the forces that build mountains, warp and crack the crust, produce strata, and cause the formation of fossils are still going on. But geologic time is so long compared with human time that in our brief life spans we see little of the constant change about us. With the publication of Lyell's *Principles of Geology,* buttressed by the work of Hutton and others, geology came of age in the early 1830's.

Trilobite

GRANITE

BASALT

PORPHYRY

IGNEOUS ROCKS

HOW ROCKS ARE FORMED

Almost all the rocks you see on the earth's surface were formed in one of three ways:

1. *Igneous rocks* have their beginning deep within the earth. As molten material beneath the crust of our planet is squeezed into or through the crust through cracks, it cools and hardens into rocks. Basalt and granite are examples of igneous rocks.

2. *Sedimentary rocks* are formed near the earth's surface. Wind, rain, frost, and other forces are constantly wearing away old rocks exposed to the air. Slowly these rocks are broken down into pebbles, sand, and mud. If the breaking-down process takes place on the land the loose materials are eventually washed onto plains, into oceans and lakes. Year after year layers of these "sediments" are laid down one on top of another. Gradually the materials making up the sediments are cemented together and form hard rock. Examples of sedimentary rocks are sandstone, clay, shale, and limestone.

3. *Metamorphic rocks* are produced by a different process. During periods of mountain folding sections of the crust are folded and pressed together. When sedimentary and igneous rocks are caught up in the folds these rocks are changed, or "metamorphosed," by the great pressure and heat. Examples of metamorphic rocks are marble, serpentine, slate, soapstone, and quartzite.

Most rocks are made up of minerals. Different kinds of granite, for instance, are produced by different mixtures of minerals. Granite that is pale and coarse is made up of the two minerals feldspar and quartz. But granite that is dark and grainy is made up of four minerals—feldspar, quartz, mica, and amphibole. Minerals are nonliving or inorganic matter. Quartz, salt, sulfur, and calcite are minerals. But not all rocks are made up of minerals. Coal, as we'll find later in this book, is made up of organic or once-living matter. What few minerals coal has are impurities mixed in with the once-living plant material which over hundreds of thousands of years turned into coal. ⟶

OBSIDIAN

SANDSTONE

LIMESTONE

CLAY

SHALE

SEDIMENTARY ROCKS

MARBLE

SERPENTINE

SLATE

QUARTZITE

METAMORPHIC ROCKS

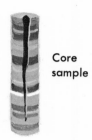

Core
sample

the ocean floor

Man is a creature of the land. Although he began his life in the sea as a creature in nature's great chain of life, today he is bonded to the land as fishes are bonded to the sea. He lives on great continental platforms that rise up out of the sea, land tables that comprise only a small thirty per cent of our planet's total surface of 197 million square miles. Yet he looks on these land masses as "typical" features of the earth and asks, as Columbia University scientist Walter H. Bucher suggests: " 'How did the vast ocean basins come to be?' Instead he might well be moved to ask: 'How did the continents come to be'?"

For many years we have regarded the oceans as extending to mysterious unknown depths, to depths where no marine life could exist. And the ocean floors we imagined as flat and featureless. But in recent years we have been forced to change our views. Columbia University scientists have now discovered tiny snail-like creatures living in an ocean trench about four miles deep where the pressure is about five tons a square inch and the temperature hovers just above freezing. Marine biologists had long thought that the last of these creatures, called Neopilina, died three hundred million years ago. Their discovery is providing us with new geological links with the past (see page 35). And in 1958 oceanographers traced part of a great undersea river "as strong as a thousand Mississippi Rivers and as swift as the Gulf Stream." It flows along the equator in an

28

easterly direction for at least thirty-five hundred miles and is sandwiched between two westerly-flowing currents. Surely there are other undersea rivers. If so, in what ways do they change the features of the ocean floor, as undersea earthquakes and volcanoes surely do? In the twentieth century we are just beginning to explore the depths of the sea, realizing that here we may find answers to questions about the earth that have puzzled scientists for a hundred years.

With echo-sounding devices geophysicists have mapped only a tiny portion of the ocean basins, considering the enormous area the basins cover. To date, scientists at Columbia's Lamont Geological Observatory have managed to collect more than twenty-five hundred samples of earth deposits resting on the sea floor. These samples plus the scientists' electronic eyes, which have scanned much of the ocean floor, tell us that the sea bottom holds a wealth of secrets about our planet's past. The mountains, cliffs, plains, and valleys visible to us on the land are mild compared with the rugged features that lie hidden in the ocean depths. Mountain ranges hundreds and thousands of miles long with peaks higher than Mt. Everest lie darkly in the Pacific deeps. When the peaks of undersea mountains rise above the water we call them islands. People of the Hawaiian Islands are living among the peaks of a group of volcanic mountains rising from the sea floor six miles below. The dark ocean waters hide gaping canyons, trenches, and valleys far deeper and broader

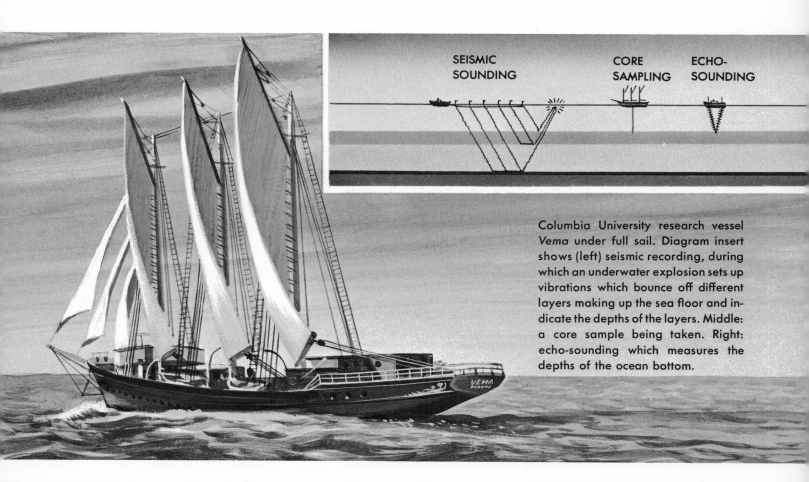

Columbia University research vessel *Vema* under full sail. Diagram insert shows (left) seismic recording, during which an underwater explosion sets up vibrations which bounce off different layers making up the sea floor and indicate the depths of the layers. Middle: a core sample being taken. Right: echo-sounding which measures the depths of the ocean bottom.

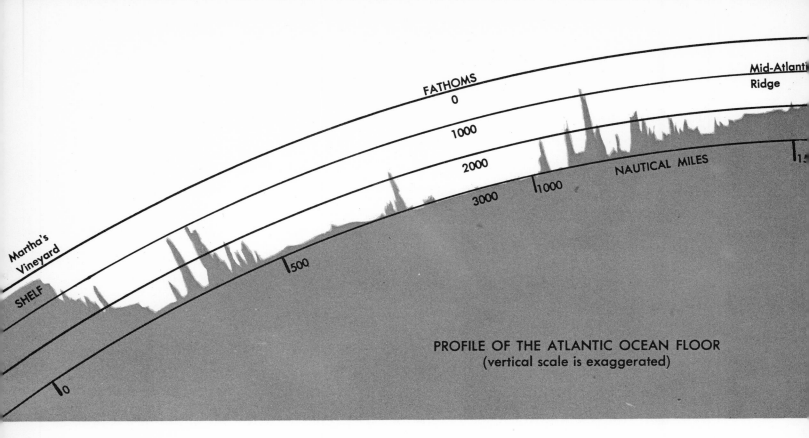

FATHOMS
0
1000
2000
3000

NAUTICAL MILES

1000

500

Martha's
Vineyard

SHELF

0

Mid-Atlantic
Ridge

PROFILE OF THE ATLANTIC OCEAN FLOOR
(vertical scale is exaggerated)

than any found on the land. For the most part the features of the ocean floor change little compared with change on the land. Rivers, sand, wind, and rain are constantly resculpturing the face of the land; but at the ocean depths erosion forces are slow-acting, so change is more slowly paced.

journey to the bottom

Not long ago maps in our geography books showed the continental land masses giving way abruptly to the sea. The land sloped gently out under the water for a short way then plunged sharply to the sea floor. With echo-sounding instruments and core-sampling devices geophysicists have altered our geography books. Today we know that the continents have shallow undersea shelves extending several miles out from the shore, then sloping sharply down to the deep sea floor. But these shelves are variable. Off New York, for example, the shelf extends more than a hundred miles, but Chile's shelf extends into the sea for only a few miles.

Not long ago we also supposed that the crust of the ocean floors was made of the same kind of rock that comprises the crust of the continents. But over the past few years scientists have discovered that this is not so. One striking difference between the sea floor and the continents is their rock make-up. The continents are nearly all granitic, lightweight rock, while the ocean floors are mostly basaltic, heavier rock. According to the

30

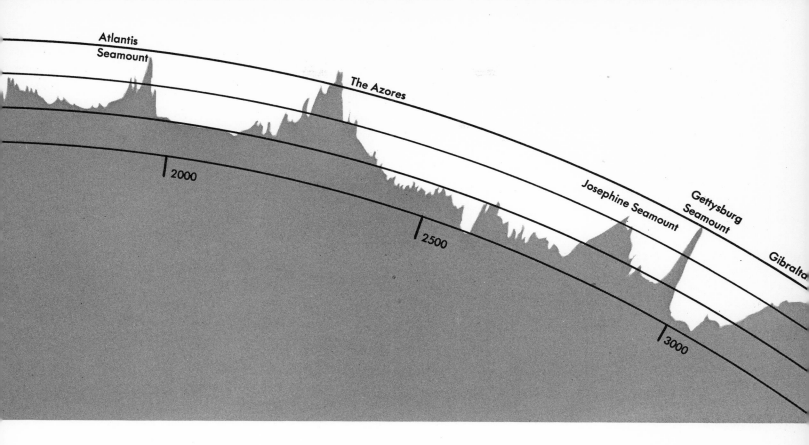

University of Toronto's J. Tuzo Wilson, we may regard the continents as "solid rafts set in a solid sea. These rafts float after a fashion, for their rocks are lighter than those of the ocean floor. In addition to rising three miles above the ocean floors their light roots of continental material sink to a depth of about fourteen miles and depress beneath them the three miles of basalt lavas corresponding to the ocean floor." There is, however, some question about whether there are two distinct layers under the continents, or whether the processes that built the continents mixed these layers up.

Before World War II Columbia's Maurice Ewing, director of the University's Lamont Geological Observatory, began to examine the edge of the North American continent off the coasts of New Jersey and Maryland. He wanted to know what happens to the granitic material making up the continent. On examining the make-up of the shelf and slope Ewing found that the granitic material did not end abruptly at the shelf's edge. Instead it extended down the slope to a depth of about two miles. Ewing next recorded the speed of earthquake surface waves along the floor of the North Atlantic. Earthquake waves, he knew, travel at different speeds through different kinds of rock. His findings in this case showed wave speeds typical of basalt, not granite. Other scientists using different methods have since reached the same conclusion: Basalt, not granite, is the typical material making up the deep ocean floors. Earlier the German geophysicist Alfred Wegener thought that America and Europe were once joined in a solid land mass. Fairly recently in geologic history, he

31

said, forces within the earth split the great continent in two (see page 46).

In Wegener's theory of granite continents drifting about in a basalt sea, the basalt would have to be relatively weak, so weak that it would not be able to support great undersea mountains; therefore the ocean floor would be essentially flat. The work of Ewing and others over the past fifteen years or so shows just the opposite. The ocean floors are fantastically rugged and rich with prominent features. Let us turn to some of these features and see how they may have come about and how they are changing today.

The continental shelves reach out from the shore for about ten to two hundred miles. And the water over the shelves' edge may be from two hundred to six hundred feet deep. At the edge of the shelves the continental slopes plunge down to the sea floor from about three to three and a half miles below. Many of the continental shelves are heaped with great thicknesses of clays, sand, and silt washed outward from the land and with organic remains of sea creatures living above the shelves. The shelves, then, can be thought of as great collecting grounds for materials washed onto them from the land. Near the edges of the shelves and along the continental slopes we find deep furrows leading down to canyons cut

The continents are great sprawling land masses whose edges are hidden by the oceans. The continental shelves may extend many miles seaward, then the continental slope plunges sharply to deep sea floor.

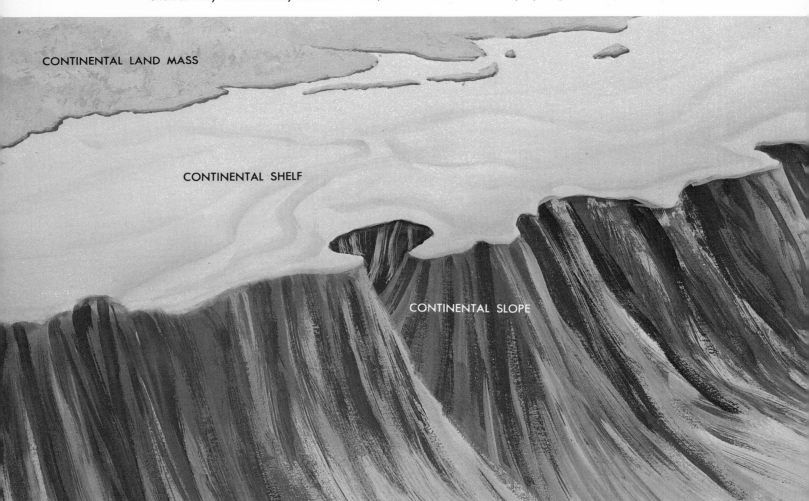

CONTINENTAL LAND MASS

CONTINENTAL SHELF

CONTINENTAL SLOPE

in the sea floor. The canyon walls, which reveal a cross section of the sediments, show the past history of the sediment collection as it was laid down age after age. Even though we have evidence that the shape of the shelves is, in part at least, determined by sediments washed onto them, the basic shape of the shelves seems to be controlled by the basement rocks underneath.

Today currents, tidal action of the water, and other forces are depositing great quantities of sediments on many of the continental shelves and slopes. After a few years to hundreds of years these sediments break loose and tumble down the slopes and onto the abyssal plains of the ocean floor. In the process they set up powerful "turbidity" currents of fifty miles an hour or more. A severe undersea earthquake that shook the coast of Newfoundland on November 18, 1929, apparently set off a giant mud avalanche that ripped across six undersea telegraph cables. "Repair crews," according to Wilson, "found that the breaks were not clean, but that scores of miles of cables were missing and that the broken ends were abraded and torn." In 1952 Ewing and B. C. Heezen examined the base of the slope and found a deposit of successive layers of sand, each layer finer toward the top. Such a deposit, they feel, was probably laid down by the great sediment slide of 1929. So the areas of ocean bottom near certain shores of the continents change year by year as the land empties billions of tons of material into the sea.

But different forces are at work changing other parts of the sea floor. In past ages weak scars, called *fissures,* in the earth's crust were strained by forces within the earth. Slowly hot molten rock from below oozed up through the great cracks and eventually towered into vast undersea chains of mountains called *ridges.* The largest mountains on the earth are not on the land, but lie hidden in the depths of the sea. The mightiest of all is the Mid-Atlantic Ridge which begins at Iceland and extends south almost to Antarctica, a distance of ten thousand miles. About five hundred miles wide at its base, the peaks of the giant ridge lie hidden a mile below the waves. A few peaks, however, stick up above the surface. We call them Iceland, St. Helena, Tristan da Cunha, Gough, Bouvet, the Azores, Ascension Island, and the Rocks of St. Paul. Mount Pico in the Azores is the highest, rising 7,613 feet above sea level. Less impressive ridges snake over the floors of the Indian and Pacific oceans. Nearly all of these undersea mountains are thought to be volcanic in origin. Only

33

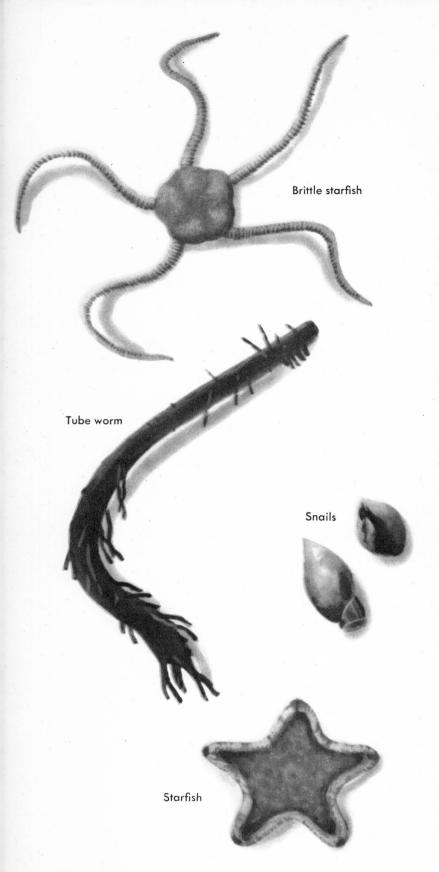

Brittle starfish

Tube worm

Snails

Starfish

SOME ANIMALS FOUND IN TRENCHES

PROFILE OF
A TRENCH

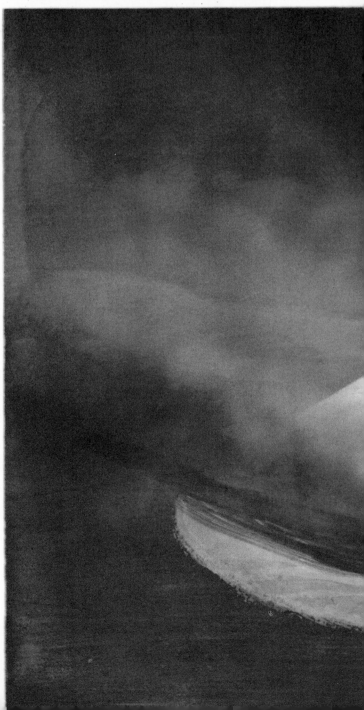

METHOD OF COLLECTING
ANIMALS FROM TRENCH

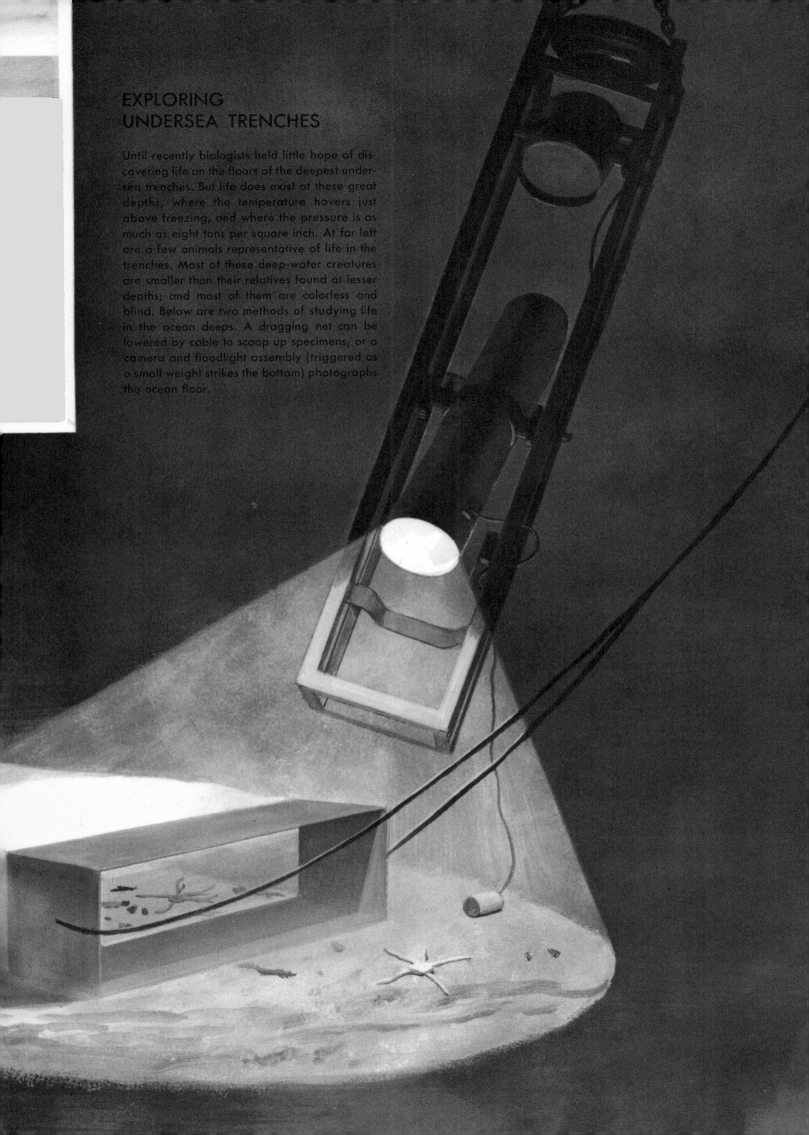

EXPLORING UNDERSEA TRENCHES

Until recently biologists held little hope of discovering life on the floors of the deepest undersea trenches. But life does exist at these great depths, where the temperature hovers just above freezing, and where the pressure is as much as eight tons per square inch. At far left are a few animals representative of life in the trenches. Most of these deep-water creatures are smaller than their relatives found at lesser depths; and most of them are colorless and blind. Below are two methods of studying life in the ocean deeps. A dragging net can be lowered by cable to scoop up specimens; or a camera and floodlight assembly (triggered as a small weight strikes the bottom) photographs the ocean floor.

"Guyots," strange formations which resemble mushroom stalks, and which may be volcanic in origin, are found in great numbers on the Pacific Ocean floor. Just how they acquired their flat tops remains a mystery.

offshore mountain-peak islands such as Newfoundland and Cuba, linked geologically to the continents, are granitic rather than basaltic.

Although the ridges are still growing today their growth is thought to be ever so slow, as it probably has been throughout their history. The reason is that the undersea volcanoes seem to erupt only occasionally. Wilson feels that the mountains have taken "a vast length of time to accumulate—very likely most of the history of the earth."

If we were able to drain half the water out of the Pacific we would expose a curious kind of submarine mountain unlike any we see on the land. Called *guyots,* they are submerged volcanic mushroom stalks with flat tops. Upward of six hundred and fifty of them are known in the Pacific, and there are a few rising out of the Atlantic sea plains. While it is easy enough to suppose that they were formed by lava spouts piling up debris over the years, it is more difficult to explain just how they acquired their flat tops which lie a half mile to a mile below the waves. One attempt to account for them suggests that in the past the ocean levels were much lower than they are today. Wave action gradually smoothed away the tops of the peaks, then the waters rose and closed over them. Another theory holds that the guyots probably always had flat tops and that their weight has pushed them slightly into the ocean floor. But the guyots are still a geophysical puzzle. The fact that shallow-water fossils have been found embedded in the tops of some suggests that at one time in their past these curious mountain caps were near the ocean surface. Beyond this scientists can say little.

Around the Pacific Ocean basin are a series of deep trenches whose black V-shaped bottoms plunge to about thirty-five thousand feet below the ocean floor. Geophysicists have also discovered trenches in the Atlantic Ocean basin. No matter where the deepest trenches are found they are remarkably alike—steep-walled on their shoreward side, shallow-walled on their ocean side and all are very nearly thirty-five thousand feet deep.

36

According to California's Scripps Institution of Oceanography scientists Robert L. Fisher and Roger Revelle: "These great gashes in the sea floor are difficult for us as land animals to visualize. It is hard to grasp the reality of a chasm so deep that seven Grand Canyons could be piled on one another in it, and so long that it would extend from New York to Kansas City. Yet these are the dimensions of the Tonga-Kermadec Trench [in the Pacific Ocean]."

To date geophysicists cannot explain why the trenches are so deep or why they are so closely associated with active volcanoes and our most intense earthquakes. Neither do they know the age of the trenches. One difficulty in answering these questions is that changes on the ocean floor take place over such long periods of time. If present-day methods of research had existed a thousand years ago, and if scientists had kept records of the changes for this long, today we would be in a much better position to answer the puzzling questions. But we do not have such records, so we are forced to base our hypothesis on the meager information at hand. After all, this is the way science works. You must have a basic idea to prove or disprove before you can arrive at knowledge.

Fisher and Revelle have suggested that the trenches may originate in this way: Deep inside our planet great sections of hot rocky material may rise toward the crust from time to time. If this happens, then quite likely upper cooler sections of material just beneath the crust are drawn downward. If so, the crust just above the cool down-moving section would be drawn downward also—forming a trench. "If this process is occurring," say Fisher and Revelle, "the earth's mantle should be cooler under the trench than elsewhere." Measurements have shown that this is so, but so few measurements have been taken to date that the theory cannot be proved.

digging into the floor

Scattered over the floors of the abyssal plains and in canyons and trenches are a variety of deposits. Among them are sand, gravel, clay of nearly every color, meteorite debris, and oozes. The oozes are the remains of billions upon billions of sea creatures which have died and accumulated on the basalt sea floor ever since the sea has supported life. By

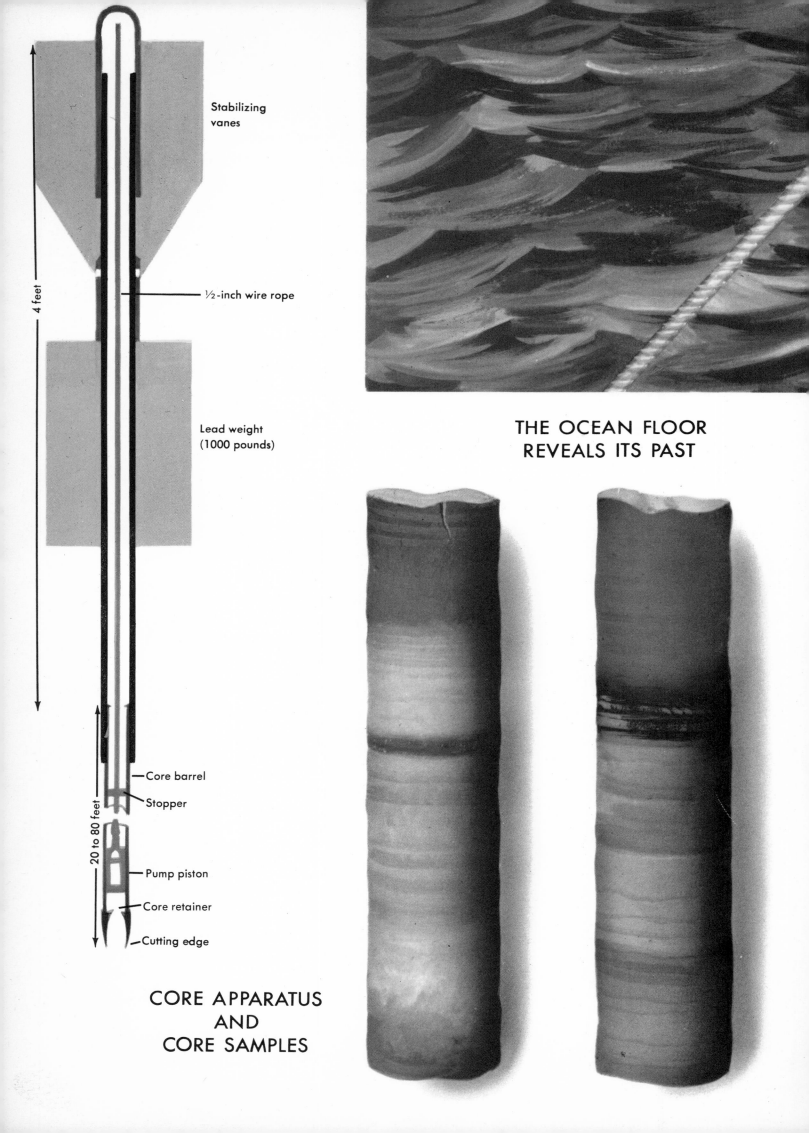

Stabilizing
vanes

½-inch wire rope

4 feet

Lead weight
(1000 pounds)

20 to 80 feet

Core barrel

Stopper

Pump piston

Core retainer

Cutting edge

CORE APPARATUS
AND
CORE SAMPLES

THE OCEAN FLOOR
REVEALS ITS PAST

Scientists aboard a Lamont Geological Observatory research ship prepare to take a "core sample." The corer is made up of a long hollow tube, guided by fins and weights, which is plunged into the sea floor. When drawn up, it contains a vertical section of sea-floor sediments dating back millions of years. By studying the cores (see left), scientists can learn much about the earth's past. One thin cross layer of a core can represent a thousand years' activity over a section of the sea floor. How the corer works is shown at far left. Core samples of seventy feet have been taken.

plunging hollow metal tubes, two and a half inches across and seventy feet long, into the sediments coating the sea floor, then studying their contents in the laboratory, scientists are learning much about the earth's geologic past. They are also learning more and more about some of the forces that are constantly changing the face of the earth under the sea.

The sedimentary layer covering the ocean bottom, according to Ewing, is on the average about two thousand feet deep. The material forming the sediments has been filtering down and settling in layers for centuries. "We have every reason to believe," he says, "that in that 2000 feet of sediment the whole history of the earth is better preserved than it is in the continental rocks...." The dream of Ewing's life is to plunge a coring tube to the very bottom of the sediments then study the telltale layers of ooze back in the laboratory. He feels that in such a sample he might find traces of some of the earth's first animals, first green plants, and primeval sediments washed into the ocean basins when the seas were formed. If Ewing's dream comes true it could be a major scientific find.

Until fairly recently geophysical explorers of the deep supposed that core samples taken nearly anywhere would show an unbroken record of the ocean floor's past. Lamont scientists, however, have changed this idea. Many of the two thousand Atlantic Ocean core samples they have taken so far show that the slow uninterrupted settling of sediments to the ocean floor is the exception, not the rule. Other forces are at work laying down deposits on the ocean bottom. Among them are deep continuous currents that carry material from the land thousands of miles over the ocean floor and the turbidity currents caused by violent undersea mud flows down continental slopes and onto the abyssal plains.

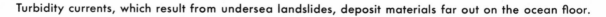

Turbidity currents, which result from undersea landslides, deposit materials far out on the ocean floor.

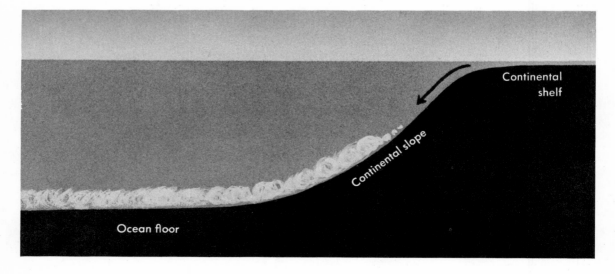

Lamont scientists became particularly interested in these turbidity currents when more and more core samples showed layers of deep-sea sand mixed between layers of sedimentary clay and ooze. For seventy-five years scientists had been trying to account for the sand and gravel found far out on the ocean floor. One theory held that over hundreds of years the winds had carried the sand out over the oceans. But could winds also carry the heavier gravel? Another said that the sands were deposited on the sea floor "at some time of greatly lowered sea level." Lamont scientists distrust both theories. They look to the turbidity currents for the answer. In their study of the Hudson Canyon off the coast of New York they have found large deposits of gravel within the canyon and deposits of sand on the plain onto which the canyon opens. They are convinced that over the years the turbidity currents have swept sand and gravel off the continental shelf, down the slope, and far out over the ocean floor. Furthermore, they feel that "erosion by turbidity currents has been an extremely important process, if not the only process, involved in the formation of the Hudson Canyon."

It appears, then, that turbidity currents may be a more important force in changing the ocean bottom than has been previously thought. Not only may they account for deep-sea canyon formation but they also must carry millions of tons of sediments yearly over the ocean floor, filling in valleys, building shallow mounds, and creating featureless plains like those found in the north Atlantic basin.

From a geophysics point of view our searches beneath the sea are just beginning. Only recently in history have we come to realize that major links with our geologic past are waiting to be discovered in the deep sediments lying undisturbed on the dark ocean floors.

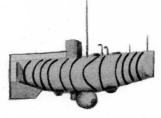

Bathyscaphe *Trieste*

41

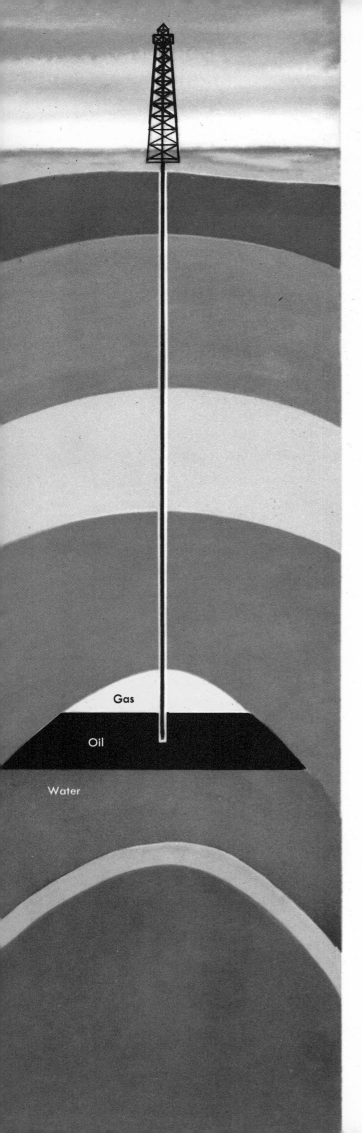

Gas

Oil

Water

THE MYSTERY OF PETROLEUM

Although petroleum is one of man's major sources of energy, exactly how and when it was formed remain a mystery. Scientists have tried to explain the origin of oil in two ways. First, they looked to the *inorganic theory* which suggested that petroleum formation was somehow linked with volcanic activity. But in recent years scientists have abandoned this theory. Today they prefer the *organic theory*, namely, that petroleum has its origin in living matter that once inhabited ancient seas.

According to the organic theory, during geologic time shallow seas covered great sections of the continents. As plants and marine animals living in the seas died, their remains sank and settled into the muddy sea floor. Bacteria acting on these organic remains caused them to decay. Meanwhile more sedimentary mud and sand settled over the decaying matter. The great weight of the sediments pressed and packed the underlying organic remains into beds of sedimentary rock (see page 26). All the while the bacteria, along with heat, pressure, and other forces, were changing the animal and plant remains into oil and gas. Age after age sedimentary rock layers sealed in layers of oil and gas. Eventually the inland seas drained off the land, leaving a firm dry crust with rich oil deposits beneath.

Is oil still being formed today? Scientists are not sure, but certain stagnant seas seem to be ideal oil-breeding areas. For instance, the upper levels of the Black Sea are rich with sea life, but the bottom waters have practically no oxygen. Instead there is a large amount of poisonous hydrogen sulfide. As sea creatures die they drift to the poisonous bottom waters and decompose slowly since there are no scavengers to eat them. Their soft bodies become entombed in the sediments and may now be awaiting the final decomposition and pressures from above which will in time change the once-living matter into oil. One thing that makes scientists look hopefully to the organic theory of oil formation is this: All the great oil fields known to us were once covered by ancient seas or now lie beneath ocean waters.　　　　——)

Right: Oil may have been formed from the decayed remains of ancient sea plants and animals, which were pressed and sealed into ancient sea floors. Left: Diagram shows oil trapped between layers of folded rock. Pressure of gas forces oil up pipe.

continents

Our planet's continents form but a small part of the earth's crust. If they were planed flat and their shavings pushed into the sea basins the ocean waters would flood our globe to a depth of about ten thousand feet. For years geophysicists have wondered how these continental granitic rafts floating in a basalt sea originated. Yet today they are little closer to the answer than were scientists of the nineteenth century. There are several theories attempting to account for the origin of continents, what has happened to them over the past three billion years or so, and how they are changing today.

As with great icebergs, only the tops of the continents are visible to the eye. Their shelves and slopes trail gently then plunge sharply to the ocean floor; the hidden bulk of the continent depresses into the mantle beneath. The striking difference between the continents and sea floors can be explained chemically: The continents are made up chiefly of *sial,* a silica-alumina material which is light in weight and color. ("Silica" is a compound of silicon and oxygen; "alumina" is a compound of aluminum and oxygen.) Because granite is the most common sialic rock, the continents are usually described as granitic. The sea floors, on the other hand, are made up chiefly of *sima,* a silica-magnesium material which is heavy and dark in color. Since basalt is the most common simatic rock the crust of the ocean floor is usually described as basaltic.

Continental land mass

Shelf

Slope

Granitic materials
(silica-alumina)

Sediments

Basaltic materials
(silica-magnesium)

The continents can be thought of as lightweight granitic "rafts" floating in a "sea" of heavy basaltic rock.

Exactly how the continents were formed is still a leading geophysical mystery. A theory that was popular several years ago describes the
earth as once being entirely crusted over with granite. Then over millions
of years forces within the earth created great cracks in the crust. The result
was huge granitic blocks, hundreds and thousands of miles across, that
crushed against each other, uplifted, tumbled, and compressed into
heaps which became the present continents. As the great blocks slid over
the basement rock below they left vast stretches of basalt bare—the ocean
floors. Another theory would have us believe that at one time in the
earth's early history a great chunk of earth-matter, which became the
moon, was torn out of the earth's side. The resulting hole is the Pacific
Ocean basin. After this gigantic rupture the remaining land mass cracked
and separated into blocks that moved to the present positions of the
continents.

Still other theories tell us that as the molten earth cooled, granitic
rocks crystallized within the earth and slowly rose to the surface as continental islands. Where the truth lies is anyone's guess. The trouble with
trying to build a continent-formation theory is simply this: We do not
know how the earth itself was formed. In a sense many geophysicists have
built their continent-formation theories on earth-formation theories of
astronomers. Today, however, geophysicists are starting with known facts
and working backwards. For example, by examining a given section of the
earth they can tell us its present composition, structure, and its age: then
by piecing together its geologic history they can deduce its possible
origin. J. Tuzo Wilson of the University of Toronto has tried to do just this.
But before we look into Wilson's work, and some of the rather surprising
facts he has turned up, let us return briefly to a man mentioned in
the last chapter—the German geologist Alfred Wegener and the theory
of floating continents.

45

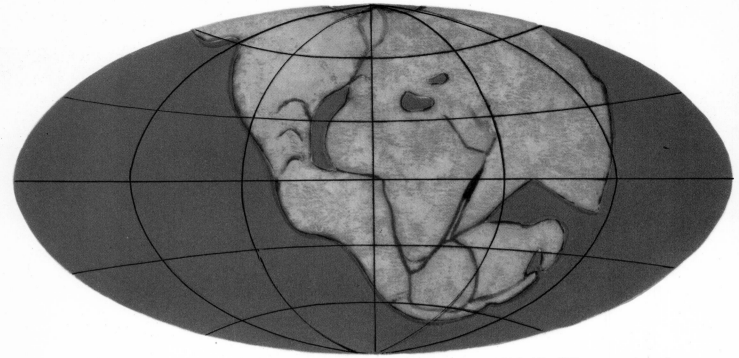

1 In 1910, Alfred Wegener suggested that the continents at the beginning of the Carboniferous were a single block—called Pan-Gaea.

continents on the move

Around 1910 Wegener was a young geologist working with a group of geographers in Greenland. Eighty-seven years earlier the British geographer Sir Edward Sabine had discovered and plotted a small island, which later became Sabine Island, off the east coast of Greenland. In 1869 another group of geographers had replotted Sabine Island, but they found that it was a quarter of a mile west of where Sabine had placed it on his maps. To Wegener's thinking this error was too great to be accounted for easily. Could it be, he asked himself, that the island, rather than the work of the geographers, is "wrong?" In short, could Sabine Island have moved westward a quarter of a mile between 1823 and 1869? Wegener himself took new measurements and found that since 1869 the island had moved westward an additional five-eighths of a mile.

Later Wegener checked the positions of other arctic land masses and came to the conclusion that all of them were drifting westward at different speeds. America supposedly was moving westward away from Europe at the rate of one-twenty-fifth of an inch every day. Armed with such data Wegener built his floating continents theory which excited geologists the world over. He envisioned an original super-continent that crystallized out of molten material making up the infant earth. Eventually the continent

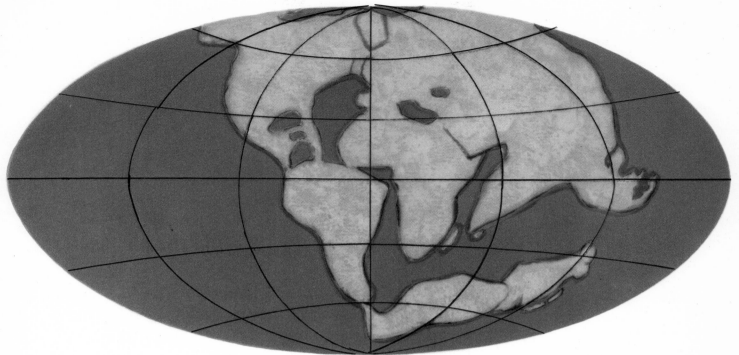

2 The primary continental block, he said, broke up. Its large pieces began to drift apart, taking the shapes of the present continents.

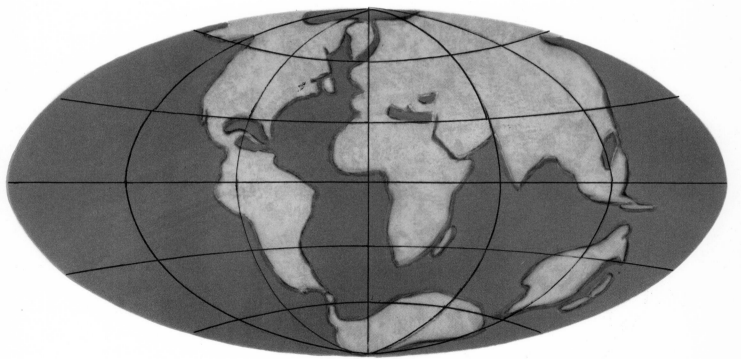

3 Today geophysicists think that the continents are on the move, but for reasons somewhat different from those Wegener proposed.

cracked and broke into several pieces. North and South America slid westward, and in the process lateral pressures caused mountainous wrinkles to rise up all along the west coast of the new continent.

Amazingly enough, the present continents do seem to fit together like pieces of a puzzle. Furthermore, some of the mountain ranges of different continents line up rather well, as if the land masses were at one time linked. As convincing as Wegener's argument appeared, many geologists refused to accept it. The result was a geological tempest which lasted twenty years or more. In 1926 the International Astronomical Union jumped into the controversy by beginning a series of measurements of its own. What the Union found seemed to add to the confusion rather than settle the argument. They discovered, for example, that Ottawa and Vancouver in 1935 were nineteen feet closer than they were in 1926. But Washington, D.C., and San Diego, California, during the same period had moved farther away from each other by some forty feet. And then came the real puzzler: The American continent, they said, was moving *toward* Europe—not away from it, as the Wegener supporters believed.

Today many geophysicists, oddly enough, are returning to the continental drift idea, but for reasons quite different from Wegener's. Ewing thinks that early in the earth's history heat currents welling up from deep inside our planet split the single supercontinent which then existed, leav-

Heavy lines in diagram show lines of weakness in the earth's crust. Over many years land masses are thought to split apart along these "rift" lines. The "drifting continent" idea, based on the rifts, seems plausible.

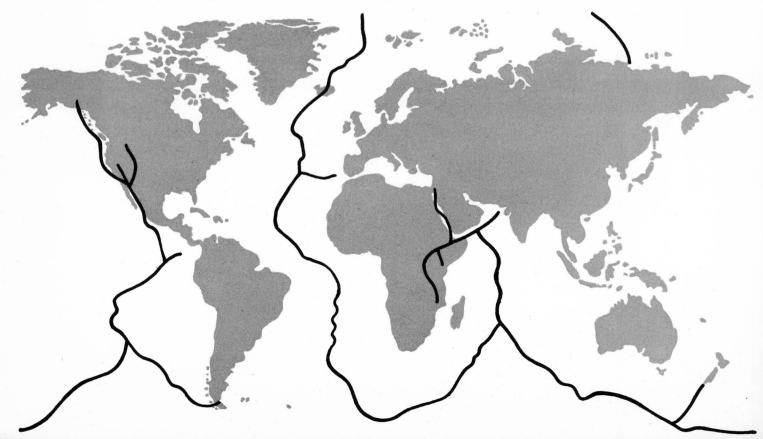

ing a rift, or crack, separating it. Rifts found over the earth's surface to-day suggest that the splitting process is still going on, helped along—as Heezen sees it—by an expansion of the planet.

The first step in the continental drift process is represented by a land mass splitting apart; for example, the young East African rifts which have split only once, so far. The second stage is represented by the Red Sea, which is an old rift with a smaller and younger rift running down the center. The third stage is represented by the Atlantic Ocean—the 3000-mile-wide "crack" which millions of years ago began as a young rift separating the supercontinent which existed when North and South America may have been joined to Europe and Africa. The Mid-Atlantic Ridge is a new rift in the older and larger rift system.

As Heezen sees it, the expansion of the planet encourages the formation of rifts by creating lines of tension and weakness, the Mid-Atlantic Ridge being one such line. Molten material, deep under the line of weakness, wells up to the surface and so forms a ridge. Gradually the ridge is broadened and a new rift forms all along its top when the ridge becomes about sixty miles wide. The Atlantic Ocean, then, may well be an old rift that is still broadening, possibly at a rate of about one yard a thousand years. And the young rifts, one along East Africa and another running north from the Gulf of California, may one day split these coastal land masses apart from their parent bodies.

"growing" continents

More recently geophysicists have looked hopefully to a theory of "growing" continents. After the oceans were formed a few "cores of continents" may have risen out of the sea here and there. Presumably these small platforms were pushed up by pressure within the earth. Geophysicists think that several such cores are recognizable today. One remains as that land mass we call Scandinavia; another is known as the Canadian Shield; and there are others in Australia and Africa.

J. Tuzo Wilson, among others, has examined some of these shields and has built a continent-formation theory on the evidence he has found. He feels that the shields are the old continental cores that rose out of the world ocean. Then over millions of years through a process of sedimentation and mountain-building the original cores grew outward from the center. He began his studies of continents by examining thousands of photographs of the Canadian Shield, then by studying its rock formations during field trips. Wilson noticed something odd. First, two areas of the Shield (one near Lake Superior, the other farther north) were flat and were made up of ancient lavas with gold running through them. And second, the remainder of the Shield circling the two flat central areas was made up of *metamorphic* rock—rocks such as sandstones and limestones that had been changed by great heat and pressure. These rocks, called *gneisses,* had been folded and twisted by some past upheaval; furthermore, they did not show any traces of gold.

Geologists had thought that the tumbled gneisses encircling the flat lava-gold area were the older rocks. But Wilson thought otherwise. By

Do continents "grow" outward from a central core? Wilson found that Canadian Shield rocks near the Great Lakes were oldest, 2.4 billion years. Outward from this area the rocks became younger, the youngest being the Atlantic coastal rocks. The medium gray area represents recently sediment-covered rocks.

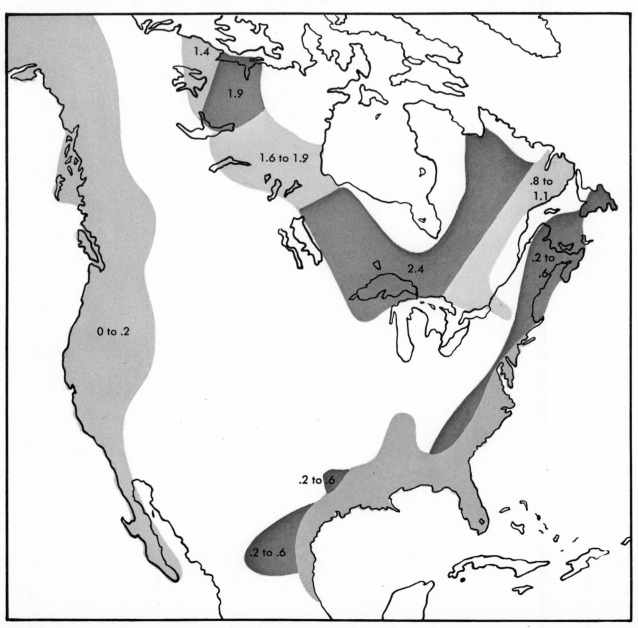

measuring the amount of radioactive decay of the rocks Wilson was able to discover their age. The central gold-bearing areas of the Shield turned out to be the oldest, about 2.5 billion years. The metamorphic rocks around the flat core were considerably younger, only 1.5 billion years; and those still farther out from the center were even younger, about one billion years. And the Atlantic coastal rocks turned out to be the youngest of all, only a half billion years or so. Does this mean, Wilson asked, that the American continent actually did grow outward from a central core of ancient lava and gold? And, if so, is the same true of other continents?

A study of the Australian and African shields tied in nicely with what Wilson had discovered about the Canadian Shield. In each case he found a central core of ancient lavas with gold running through them. And rimming the core were younger rocks. The pattern seemed most promising; but so have other geologic patterns. Columbia's Marshall Kay warns: "There do seem to be belts of progressively younger intrusions around the central part of the Canadian Shield. But on the other hand there are dated rocks that seem pretty old in far-flung parts of the continent—such as Colorado and Texas. So probably it is not as simple as one might like it to be." Time alone will decide the fate of this continent-formation theory.

A host of other questions crossed Wilson's mind during his investigations. Assuming that his idea was sound, he wondered why the cores of continents should have remained flat and almost unchanged over the years while the outer regions apparently had been twisted and crushed by mountain-building processes. Today geophysicists look to "island arcs" as a possible answer to this question.

island arcs

If the continents did begin as small cores rising out of the sea, then we can paint the following picture of how they may have grown over a period of millions upon millions of years. Rain and wind would have eroded the primitive continents, washing their sediments into the sea. A portion of these sediments would collect on the shallow continental shelves while most of the remainder would form a thick deposit at the base of the continental slope. Through forces not clearly understood, sediments that slid down

51

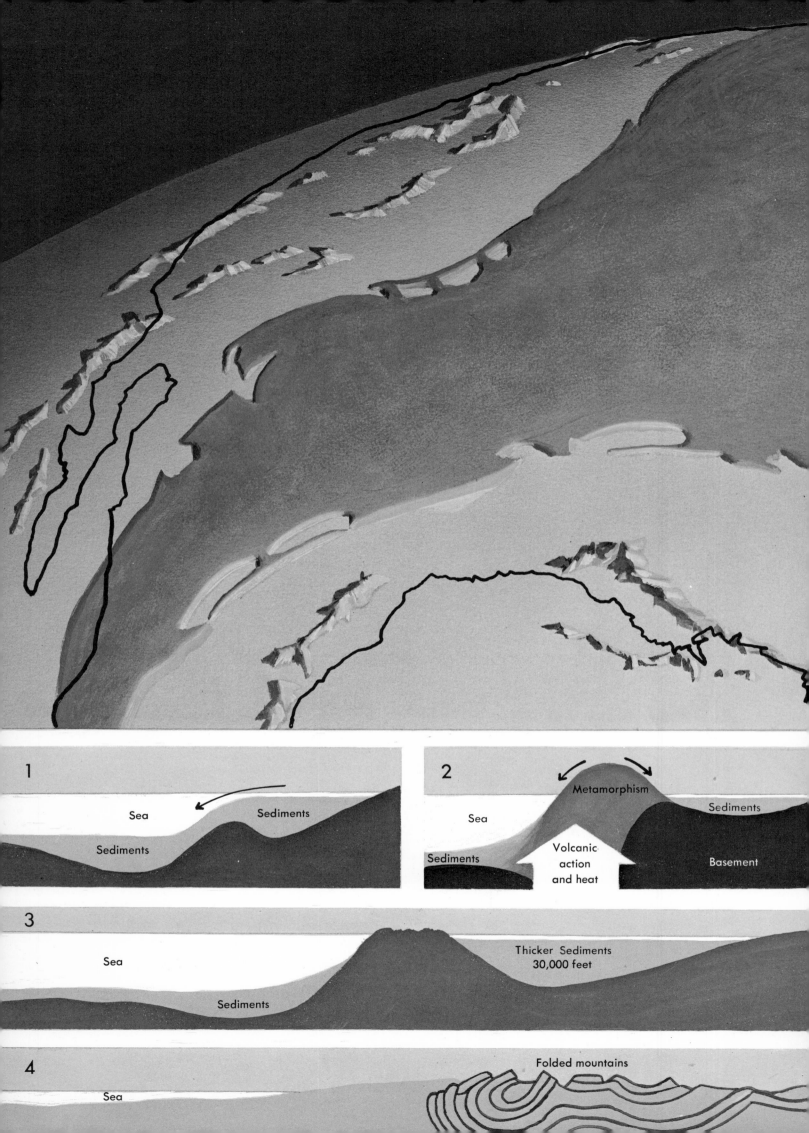

1

Sea

Sediments

Sediments

2

Metamorphism

Sea

Sediments

Volcanic action and heat

Sediments

Basement

3

Sea

Thicker Sediments 30,000 feet

Sediments

4

Sea

Folded mountains

HOW CONTINENTS "GROW"

Four hundred million years ago, North America may have been shaped as shown by the gray area above. Gradually, over millions of years, sediments were washed off the land and accumulated in the offshore sea (1, in diagrams at left). Volcanic action and heat next pushed the offshore land up (2), resulting in the "island arcs" shown ringing the solid land mass. Over thousands or millions or more years, more sediments accumulated in the shallow sea between the island arcs and the mainland (3). A second uplift raised the offshore sea bottom high above sea level, in the process folding the sedimentary rocks (4). The result was a new shape for the continent (indicated by black outline showing Florida and the Gulf of California).

the continental slope would eventually be heated, contorted, and masses of volcanics would be added to them. During this process they would be lifted until they formed an island arc separated from the mainland by a broad, shallow sea. Further erosion would contribute more sediments to this shallow sea, as well as to the region offshore, until another uplift, this time unaccompanied by heat and volcanism, raised this area high above sea level and folded and faulted the sedimentary rocks within it.

We can see this process in various stages of its development in different parts of the world. An early stage is off the eastern coast of the United States where thousands of feet of sediments are collected on the continental shelf and even more thousands of feet at the base of the continental slope. At a later stage the process is going on in the East China Sea. The outer arc of the Japanese islands is already in evidence, and the shallow China Sea is being filled partly from sediments washed from these islands and partly by thousands of tons of sediments poured into it yearly by the Hwang Ho and Yangtze rivers. A mature stage is that of the Appalachian mountain system where the outer arc is now worn down to a region of low relief covering much of the middle Atlantic and southeastern states while the younger folded sedimentary mountains still reach elevations in excess of 6000 feet above sea level.

In an endless process, for man at least, the land seems to be gaining over the sea as the continents creep steadily into the ocean deeps. Mountain arcs are raised, join the land, and in time are worn smooth and flat by wind and rain. Telltale fossils and rocks, which have been altered by great heat and pressure, are the signposts indicating that changes have taken place in the past. But man can see the grandeur of the process of change only in his imagination.

land bridges

The distribution of plant and animal life over the earth shows us that the continents have not always been separated by seas. At one time in our geologic past great land bridges may have joined some of the continents. Also, where there are now seas there was once land; and where there was once land there are now seas.

Biological evidence suggests that from time to time nearly every part of the land was probably sea-covered. High in the Himalayas, in the

Andes, and Alps are fossil remains of marine animals. About eighty million years ago North America rose from a sea that had covered it for millions of years. When it emerged, an inland sea known as Lake Laramie was left in a great hollow in the middle of the continent. Scientists think that during other geologic time periods land bridges crossed the Atlantic Ocean at many places: from West Africa to Venezuela and the Guianas; from Spain and North Africa to the east coast of the United States; and from northern Europe to Greenland and Labrador. An enormous continent called Gondwana one time supposedly sprawled over parts of Africa, Asia, Australia, and South America. In time it eroded away, or sank, leaving a land bridge called Lemuria which linked Madagascar and India, then ended as an island chain. Western Europe at one time extended beyond the British Isles. What is now the English Channel was once a wide sunny plain along which the river Seine flowed.

The majestic changes that have taken place on the land and beneath the sea are staggering to the imagination. Yet their records are preserved, for a time at least, in the rocks and mountains and deep beneath the seas.

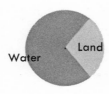

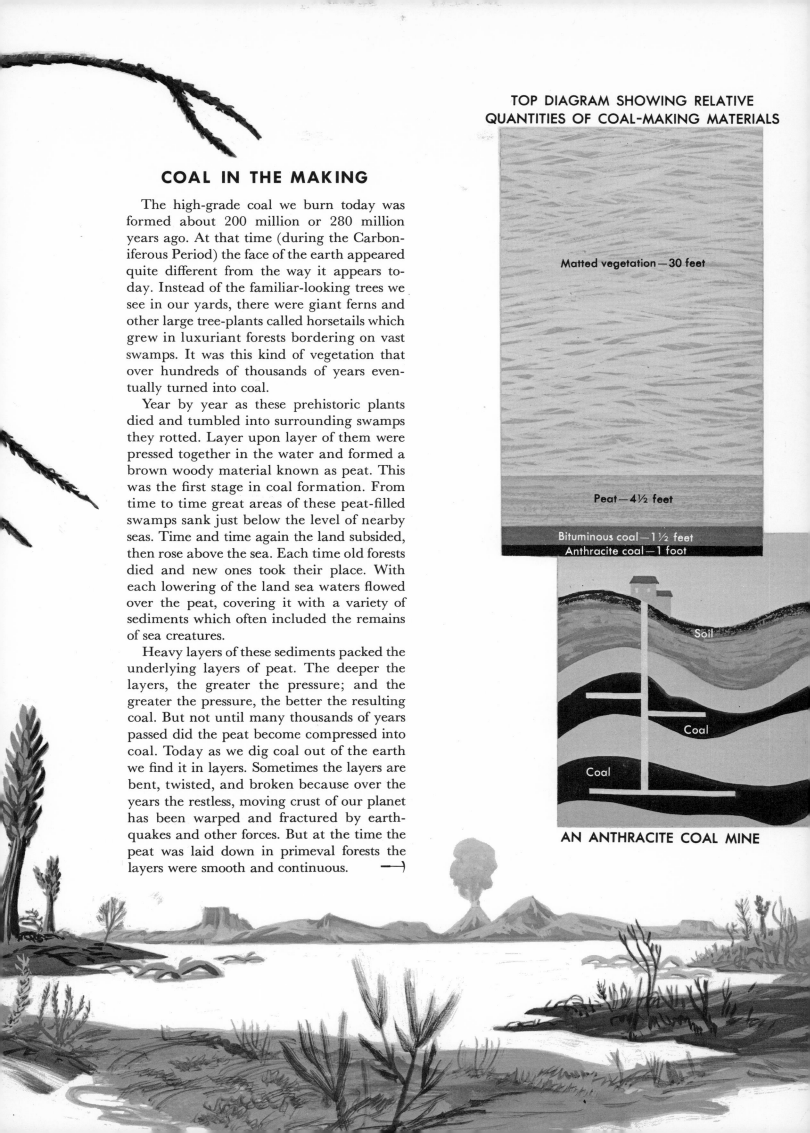

COAL IN THE MAKING

The high-grade coal we burn today was formed about 200 million or 280 million years ago. At that time (during the Carboniferous Period) the face of the earth appeared quite different from the way it appears today. Instead of the familiar-looking trees we see in our yards, there were giant ferns and other large tree-plants called horsetails which grew in luxuriant forests bordering on vast swamps. It was this kind of vegetation that over hundreds of thousands of years eventually turned into coal.

Year by year as these prehistoric plants died and tumbled into surrounding swamps they rotted. Layer upon layer of them were pressed together in the water and formed a brown woody material known as peat. This was the first stage in coal formation. From time to time great areas of these peat-filled swamps sank just below the level of nearby seas. Time and time again the land subsided, then rose above the sea. Each time old forests died and new ones took their place. With each lowering of the land sea waters flowed over the peat, covering it with a variety of sediments which often included the remains of sea creatures.

Heavy layers of these sediments packed the underlying layers of peat. The deeper the layers, the greater the pressure; and the greater the pressure, the better the resulting coal. But not until many thousands of years passed did the peat become compressed into coal. Today as we dig coal out of the earth we find it in layers. Sometimes the layers are bent, twisted, and broken because over the years the restless, moving crust of our planet has been warped and fractured by earthquakes and other forces. But at the time the peat was laid down in primeval forests the layers were smooth and continuous. ——➔

TOP DIAGRAM SHOWING RELATIVE QUANTITIES OF COAL-MAKING MATERIALS

Matted vegetation—30 feet

Peat—4½ feet

Bituminous coal—1½ feet

Anthracite coal—1 foot

Soil

Coal

Coal

AN ANTHRACITE COAL MINE

Surface waves

earthquakes

The time is one minute and twenty-eight seconds before noon, September 1, 1923. The place, Japan. The day had begun much like any other day, except for early morning squalls of a dying storm. At the noon hour women shoppers, delivery boys, business men, and school children were preparing for lunch. There was no sign, no warning, nothing to tell them that the greatest earthquake disaster in history was about to crumble the fragile cities of Tokyo and Yokohama. In fact, many people had been lulled into believing that the Tokyo area probably would be free of major earthquakes for a century or more.

(Fusakichi Omori, professor of seismology at Tokyo University, had made the prediction after studying the earthquake of April 26, 1922. The April quake was the principal shock of a series, he had thought, and most likely Tokyo residents would feel only mild tremors for quite some time afterward. But Omori and others had long been unhappy about Tokyo's ability to survive a real earthshaker. Since 1905 they had felt that the city's water-supply system and fire-fighting equipment should be improved so that the fires that generally follow a major quake could be controlled. But like many other farsighted warnings this one aroused little concern.)

Then on September 1, 1923 it happened.

On that fateful day the earth beneath the waters of Sagami Bay snapped. Sharp vibrations fanned out to Yokohama, some fifty miles away, and then quivered on to Tokyo, some seventy miles away. The most violent shakes lasted about thirty seconds, then came a series of rapid, less severe aftershocks lasting several minutes. Professor Akitune Imamura at Tokyo University described the earthquake in these words:

"At first, the movement was rather slow and feeble, so I did not take it to be the forerunner of so big a shock. . . . Soon the vibration became large, and after three or four seconds from the commencement, I felt the shock to be very strong indeed. Seven or eight seconds passed and the building was shaking to an extraordinary extent, but I considered these movements not yet to be the principal portion. At the twelfth second from

Within twelve hours after the Japan earthquake of 1923, fire had destroyed more than half of Yokohama. By the time the fires finally died out, the entire city was gutted. The epicenter of the quake was Sagami Bay.

the start . . . came a very big vibration, which I took at once to be the beginning of the principal portion. Now the motion, instead of becoming less and less as usual, went on increasing in intensity very quickly, and after four or five seconds I felt it to have reached its strongest. During this time the tiles were showering down from the roof making a loud noise, and I wondered whether the building could stand or not. . . . During the following ten seconds the motion, though still violent, became somewhat less severe, and its character gradually changed, the vibrations becoming slower but bigger. For the next few minutes we felt an undulatory movement like that on a boat in windy weather, and we were now and then threatened by severe aftershocks. After five minutes from the beginning, I stood up and went over to see the [seismograph] instruments. . . .

"Soon after the first shock, fire broke out at two places in the university, and within one and a half hours our Institute was enveloped in raging smoke and heat. . . . I cannot tell you how desperately I fought against the fire without water or any help from the outside. It was ten o'clock at night before I found our Institute and Observatory quite safe. . . . We all, ten in number, did our best, partly in continuing earthquake observations and partly in extinguishing the fire, taking no food or drink till midnight, while four of us who were residing in the lower part of the town lost our houses and property by fire."

The lower part of Tokyo, built on soft soil and fill, suffered the worst damage from the earthquake itself. The upper part of town, which was built on firmer ground, was somewhat better off. Nevertheless fifty-four per cent of Tokyo's brick buildings and ten per cent of its reinforced concrete buildings were destroyed or badly damaged. Of sixteen steel frame buildings, only six were unharmed. The shifting and shaking ground throughout the city bent and snapped water lines. So by the time the hundreds of fires that broke out reached full force and swept over the city the fire department was helpless. Within thirty minutes after the earthquake began 136 fires had broken out in Tokyo alone. After fifty-six hours a total of 366,262 houses were gone—seventy-one per cent of Tokyo's homes. The Yokohama fire was more severe. Within twelve hours more than half the city was in total ruin, and by the time the last fires died out the entire city was gutted.

The death toll for the areas affected by the earthquake, then gripped by fire, finally reached about a hundred thousand. An additional hundred thousand people were injured and about forty-three thousand were missing. In Tokyo during the remainder of September seismographs recorded a total of 1,256 aftershocks.

TEN FAMOUS EARTHQUAKES

PLACE	DATE	WHAT HAPPENED
Lisbon, Portugal	1755	More than 20,000 killed; three shocks leveled part of the city; fires and a "tidal" wave or tsunami.
Charleston, South Carolina	1886	Most severe quake on Atlantic coast; shocks felt over nearly 3,000,000 square miles. Tremors felt as far north as Boston.
Assam, India	1897	Farmland and jungle flooded; nearly all stone buildings in area shaken to ground; hills around Assam uplifted from five to twenty feet.
Kangra, India	1905	About 20,000 killed; shocks felt over area of 1,500,000 square miles.
California	1906	About 1000 killed. Crust snapped along 270-mile length. San Francisco destroyed by fire.
Messina and Reggio, Italy	1908	About 100,000 killed; people trapped in narrow streets as poorly constructed buildings tumbled on them; tsunami also caused damage.
Kansu, China	1920	About 200,000 killed; hundreds of towns destroyed.
Concepcion, Chile	1939	About 30,000 killed; about twenty towns destroyed.
Central Turkey	1939	About 50,000 killed; many towns and villages destroyed by series of shocks.
Tibet, China, Burma, India	1950	Uplifting mountains in Tibet changed geography of quake region.

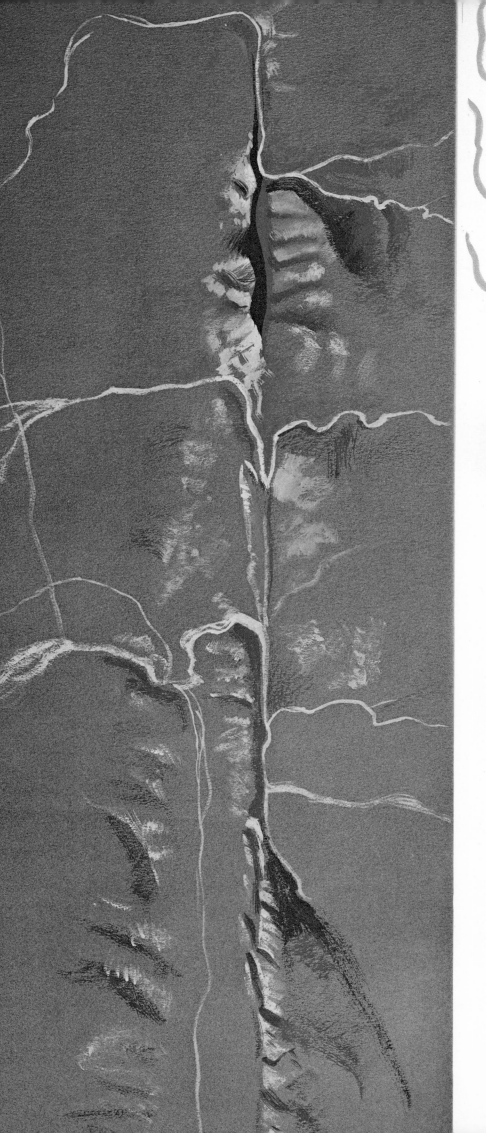

Cape Mendocino

CALIFORNIA

San Francisco

San Juan

Heavy line shows part of fault line that snapped.

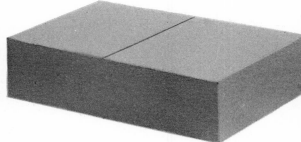

In 1800 the ground along both sides of the San Andreas Fault was at "rest" (see text, page 63).

The 1906 earthquake displaced a road at the head of Tomales Bay by a distance of twenty-one feet.

Horizontal shifting of the ground disturbed this orange grove in California's Imperial Valley, 1940.

Left: View of six-hundred-mile San Andreas Fault. (*U. S. Forest Service*)

In the San Francisco earthquake of 1906, fire accounted for about ninety-five per cent of the total damage.

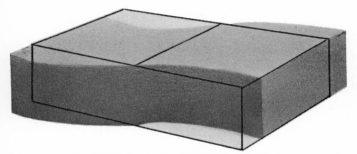

By 1875 the ground along the fault was warped; this caused tensions along its entire length.

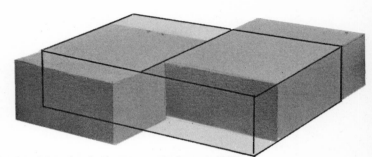

April 18, 1906, the fault snapped along a 270-mile section, setting up earthquake vibrations.

faults and tsunami

During the Japan earthquake of 1923 a great *fault,* or crack, appeared along the bottom of Sagami Bay. A fault is nothing more than a break in the earth's crust. Year after year the two surfaces along a fault may press against each other without causing a disturbance. But after a while the pressure may become so great that the two surfaces slip, or snap (see diagram of San Andreas Fault, this page). When the snapping takes place violent vibrations shiver through the ground and may topple buildings for miles around. Thousands, if not millions, of faults thread their way over the globe, but just how deeply these great cracks extend into the earth is still a mystery.

One of the most spectacular faults visible to man is located in California and is known as the San Andreas Fault. This break in the earth's crust extends for some six hundred miles across California's coastal ranges of mountains. According to Harvard seismologist L. Don Leet, around 1800 the fault was "at rest." But gradually over the next 106 years forces

63

within the earth strained the fault, shoving and twisting it to cause tension along its facing surfaces. By 1875 the ground along the fault was warped. Then on the morning of April 18, 1906, the fault snapped along a 270-mile section, from Upper Mattole in Humboldt County to San Juan in San Benito County. The resulting vibrations traveled around the world. When the fault snapped the ground along it shifted horizontally, producing some bizarre effects. At the head of Tomales Bay a road crossing the fault was broken in two; one part of it jumped to the right, the other part to the left. Its two new ends were displaced from one another by twenty-one feet. In other cases fences were offset by several feet. Near Olema the front walk of a ranch house hopped several feet in one direction while the house itself hopped several feet in the opposite direction.

San Francisco, only ten miles away from the fault, was hard hit when the fault snapped. Within a minute after the fault jolted the surrounding land, all of the damage resulting from the earth's shaking had been done. Along with several buildings in downtown San Francisco the new seven-million-dollar City Hall collapsed. Other buildings, their foundations rooted in soft soil, were twisted and cracked, but those standing on rock foundations escaped with little damage. As in the case of the Japan earthquake, the fire that followed the San Francisco quake accounted for about ninety-five per cent of the damage. Loss by fire in San Francisco alone was estimated at four hundred million dollars.

When faults snap on land their destructiveness is limited to the vibrations they set up. But when they snap along the sea floor they may set up "tidal" waves, which seismologists prefer to call *tsunami* since these waves have nothing to do with the tide. When an undersea fault snaps up and down, rather than from side to side, a mound of water suddenly forms at the surface. At this stage gravity acts to level the water. The result is a series of broad waves that travel at speeds near five hundred miles an hour. Ships at sea do not notice tsunami since each wave may be not more than two or three feet high with a distance of a hundred miles or more between them. But as the waves near shallow water the sea along the shore rises rapidly. The level builds up because the front of the wave is slowed by shallow water as the back of the wave piles up on the water ahead. Finally, the tsunami sweeps over any coastal villages in the way with terrible destructive force. On October 6, 1737, one of the greatest tsunami on record flooded the coast of Cape Lopatka on the

64

southern tip of Kamchatka Peninsula, part of Siberia. By the time the wave reached shore it towered 210 feet into the air. On June 15, 1896, an undersea earthquake 125 miles offshore from the Sanriku district of Japan set up a tsunami that swept in and broke a hundred feet high onto the shore. After the waters receded twenty-seven thousand bodies and debris from more than ten thousand houses lay strewn about.

Faulting is not the only cause of earthquakes. In fact some scientists have suggested that faulting is a result, not a cause, of earthquakes. R. D. Oldham of England, for example, for many years felt that all severe earthquakes were caused by large volumes of matter deep inside the earth shifting about with explosive violence. In addition to sending elastic waves throughout the earth, he said that these underground shifts also caused faulting near the surface. More recently Japanese seismologists have thought that *magma,* or molten rock, beneath the earth's crust moves about and causes earthquakes. Great pools of magma, they say, change from time to time chemically and physically. When the pressure in a pool builds up sufficiently the molten rock is violently ejected into weaker, neighboring rock. This sudden motion of magma supposedly sets up the vibrations that produce tremors on the surface. To support this theory the Japanese seismologists point to changes in land level observed in Japan after large earthquakes. The changes in level, they maintain, are evidence of pressure changes within the magma cavities.

Superstitions "explaining" earthquakes are so numerous that we will not attempt to catalog them. Perry Byerly of the University of California sums up his feeling about such superstitions in these words: "There seems always to be a legion of nonscientists who are attempting to establish as direct causes of earthquakes some activity in the heavens. They attempt this without first mastering what is already known about earthquakes and astronomy. . . . They remind one of a man who goes to a bridge tournament with a set of rules of his own and a brand new method of keeping score. . . . "

earthquake waves 65

Whenever an earthquake bumps, jars, or shakes our planet, however slightly, complex waves are sent out from the *focus,* or place where the

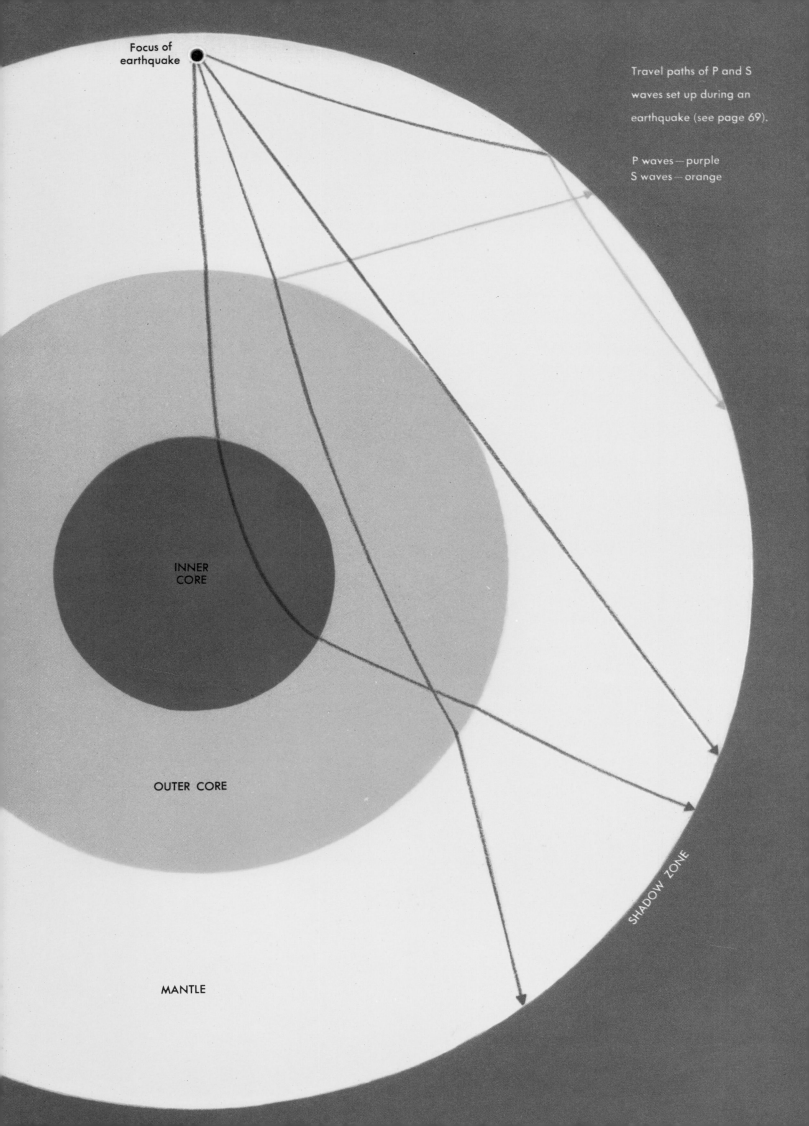

Focus of earthquake

Travel paths of P and S waves set up during an earthquake (see page 69).

P waves—purple
S waves—orange

INNER CORE

OUTER CORE

SHADOW ZONE

MANTLE

earthquake occurs. There are "body waves" that pass through the earth; and there are "surface waves" which shiver around the earth along its curved surface.

The first kind of wave that is recorded by earthquake instruments, called seismographs, is the *push* or *compressional* wave. When an underground fault snaps, the resulting bump is passed on to neighboring rock, which passes the bump on to rock still farther away, and so on until the wave reaches the surface. You can set up push waves of your own by striking the end of a steel rod with a hammer. The particles of metal struck by your hammer at the tip of the rod are first compressed then expand as they return to their normal shape. When they expand they compress the particles farther along the rod, and so on to the opposite end. In this way the blow you struck is passed on from particle to particle all along the length of the rod. Seismologists also call the push wave a longitudinal wave because of the way it travels. They write it as a P wave (the P standing for "primary" because this wave travels the fastest and reaches the seismograph ahead of all other waves sent out by an earthquake).

The second kind of wave that reaches the seismograph is the *shake,* or *shear* wave. Because this wave takes second place in the running it is written as an S wave (the S standing for "secondary"). You can set up shake waves by striking a metal rod along the side, rather than on the end. This will produce an up-and-down motion of metal particles in the rod, and this particle motion is carried to the opposite end of the rod as a wave. Now what happens if you strike a glancing blow at the end of a metal rod in such a way that you set up both P and S waves? Because the P waves travel faster, the end of the rod will begin vibrating back and forth a fraction of a second before the S waves make it vibrate up and down.

During an earthquake both P and S waves leave the focus at the same time. But because the S waves travel only two-thirds the speed of

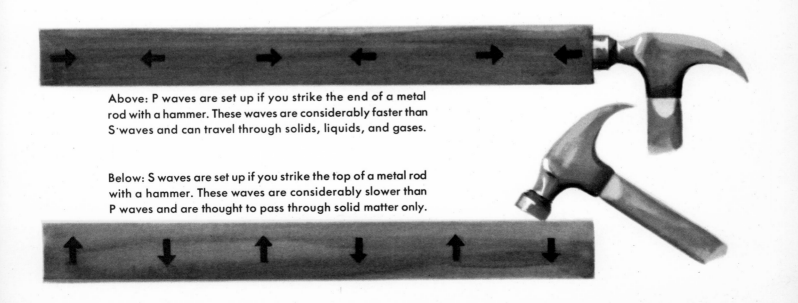

Above: P waves are set up if you strike the end of a metal rod with a hammer. These waves are considerably faster than S·waves and can travel through solids, liquids, and gases.

Below: S waves are set up if you strike the top of a metal rod with a hammer. These waves are considerably slower than P waves and are thought to pass through solid matter only.

the P waves, the P waves are felt first. For example, a P wave will travel a hundred miles twenty seconds faster than the S wave, or two thousand miles two minutes and fifty-four seconds faster than the S wave. When the P and S waves reach the surface of our globe they set up a third kind of wave called *surface* waves. These waves are the slowest of all and appear as long waves on a seismogram (see page 72). The surface waves are the ones that cause damage during an earthquake.

As seismologists have discovered more about the behavior of earthquake waves they have been able to put the waves to work and so learn about the deep interior of our planet. For example, an important thing they have discovered about the waves is this: The P waves can travel through solids, liquids, or gases. The reason is that the particles making up all three can be compressed. But the S waves can travel through only those materials whose shape can be changed—meaning solids only. The molecules of liquids and gases slip around each other too easily, so they cannot transmit shake waves. With the knowledge that P and S waves travel at different speeds, and knowing that they behave differently in different kinds of materials, seismologists should be able to tell us something about the earth's interior. They have done just this.

JEFFREYS-BULLEN TRAVEL TIME TABLE
FOR "P" AND "S" WAVES

REGION	NAME	DEPTH IN MILES	P VELOCITY (MILES PER SEC.)	S VELOCITY (MILES PER SEC.)
A	— Crust	0–25	Widely variable	Widely variable
B	— Mantle	25–250	5.0–5.6	2.7–3.1
C		250–600	5.6–7.1	3.1–4.0
D'		600–1700	7.1–8.5	4.0–4.6
D"		1700–1800	8.5	4.6
E	— Outer Core	1800–3100	5.0–6.8	0?
F	— Transition Region	3100–3200	6.8–6.0	?
G	— Inner Core	3200–3960	7.0–7.1	?

In 1906 Oldham proved that the earth had a central core made of a material quite different from the outer parts of the earth. What led him to think this was his study of P waves as they traveled through the earth. He discovered a "shadow zone" caused as P waves were refracted, or bent, by some special material making up the core of our planet. In studying the diagram, imagine an earthquake with its focus at the North Pole. P waves speed outward in all directions, but as they strike some denser material deep within the earth they are pulled off course and bent in a new direction. The result is a shadow zone nearly empty of P waves. Seismologists the world over cheered Oldham's discovery. Soon a new discovery was made about the earth's core. S waves apparently were not passing through it. Since S waves cannot pass through liquids, could the new-found core be some kind of molten material? The answer seemed to be yes. The original earth's supply of molten iron must have flowed toward the center of our planet and formed a huge molten core. The exact size of this core was worked out by Beno Gutenberg of the California Institute of Technology in 1912. He placed the core's outer boundary at eighteen hundred miles below the surface. The molten iron core, then, appeared to make up more than half the earth's body. But the story of the earth's interior did not end here.

A Danish seismologist, Miss I. Lehmann, began studying a few P waves that sometimes managed to enter the shadow zone (see page 66). But how were they getting through? She concluded that within the molten core there must be a smaller solid core that speeded up the P waves and bent them so sharply that they skipped right into the shadow zone. Harold Jeffreys in England agreed with Miss Lehmann's findings and figured that the inner solid core (of iron) is a ball sixteen hundred miles in diameter. Now the picture of the earth's interior seemed fairly complete.

Above our planet's outer core is the mantle and the thin crust we walk on. Studies of how P and S waves travel through this outer section tell us about its make-up. One thing seismologists have learned is that the speed of both P and S waves changes greatly within the crust. This is true down to a depth of about twenty to thirty miles. Because both P and S waves travel through the crust, and because their speeds vary, seismologists could conclude that the crust is made up of solid (rocky) materials of varying densities. But what lies just below this thin crust? And what happens to P and S waves in this slightly deeper region?

In 1909 the Croatian seismologist A. Mohorovičić was studying the wave patterns produced by a Balkan earthquake. He found that at a depth of some twenty miles the speed of P and S waves increased and continued increasing until they reached the core. Since their speed increases, then the material they pass through must be considerably denser than the above-lying rocks. Today geophysicists think that the material making up the mantle is some iron-magnesium silicate like oviline under extremely high pressure—so high that the material, although above its melting point at sea level, behaves like a solid. Here, then, was a new discontinuity, or boundary, dividing the crust from the mantle. It became known as the *M discontinuity,* after Mohorovičić.

Earthquake waves have given us a picture of the interior of the earth. We walk on a thin, solid rocky crust twenty to thirty miles deep. Below is the plastic mantle reaching to a depth of about eighteen hundred miles. And at the center is the earth's core consisting of two parts—an outer core of iron reaching down to a depth of about thirty-one hundred miles and an inner core of iron penetrating to the earth's center, 3960 miles below the surface.

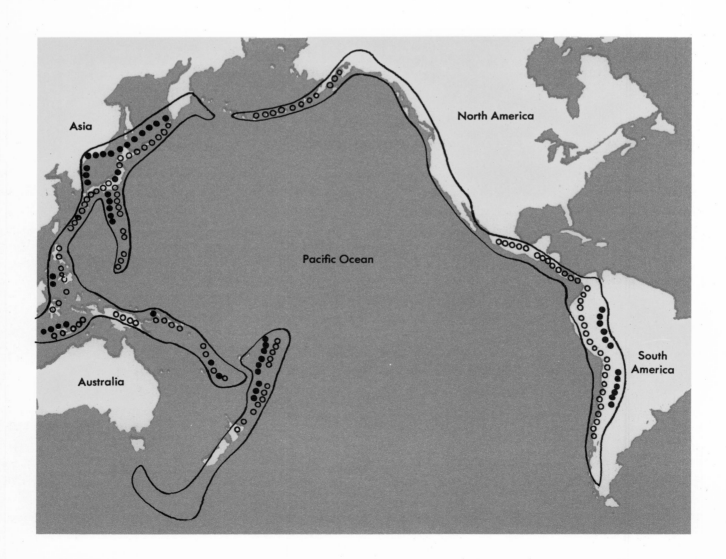

deep focus earthquakes

The "rim of fire," so named because most of the world's active volcanoes rim the Pacific Ocean basin, is highly earthquake active. Light dots in the diagram represent earthquakes that take place from about ten to forty miles underground. But there are also deep focus earthquakes (heavy dots), or those that take place about 185 miles and more within the earth. Rarely do deep focus quakes cause damage on the surface, although they are recorded by seismographs. Areas of deep focus earthquakes include inland South America (450 miles deep); Japan (220 miles deep); Hindu Kush Mountains of the Himalayas (140 miles deep). To date the deepest shock recorded took place at a depth of 435 miles, south of Celebes. The baffling part about deep earthquakes is to explain how they are caused. Some geophysicists think that faults snapping deep within the earth cause them. But others feel that the plastic rock at the depths mentioned must flow, rather than snap, when pressure changes take place; so faulting may not be the cause. However, underground explosions, they feel, could cause the deep quakes.

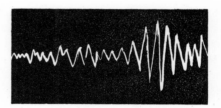

THE SEISMOGRAPH STATION

Earthquakes are recorded on instruments called "seismographs." The wave pattern these instruments trace are known as "seismograms." In principle the seismograph is a pendulum with a fine-point pen hanging from it. Beneath the pen is a drum of paper that rotates day and night. When all is quiet the pen traces a straight line on the moving paper. When an earthquake shakes the seismograph station, the frame supporting the pendulum moves, as the entire building does, but the pendulum does not. The result is an inked wiggly line that shows when the earthquake occurred and how severe it was. The more pronounced the wiggles, the more severe the earthquake.

In practice, a seismograph station has three seismographs. One records the up-and-down motion of the earth during a quake and the other two record horizontal motions (one aligned north-south, the other east-west).

As soon as an earthquake broadcasts its effects scientists want to know when it took place and where its epicenter is. (The epicenter is the point on the surface above the focus of the quake.) The time the earthquake tremors shake the seismograph station is obtained simply by looking at the seismogram which is marked off in hours, minutes, and seconds. Next, the distance of the earthquake from the station is learned. This is done by reading the P and S waves (see page 68) traced out. Since P waves travel faster than S waves, the P waves will be first to wiggle onto the rotating drum. The farther away from the station the earthquake is, the greater the time gap between the appearance of P and S waves. As soon as the seismologist determines the time gap, he consults a set of tables which gives him the distance of the quake. For example, if the S waves reach the seismograph six minutes and forty seconds behind the P waves, then the epicenter of the quake is found to be 3,050 miles away from the recording station.

But this information alone is not enough to tell the seismologist just where the quake took place. At this stage he knows only the time and distance of the quake, not its direction away from the station. To pinpoint the quake the seismologist waits for reports from two other stations. When he learns the distance of the quake from these other stations, he then draws three circles. The distance of the quake from station A is the radius of circle A, and the center of circle A is station A. The same procedure is followed for circles B and C. The point at which the three circles intersect (see diagram) is the epicenter of the earthquake.　　　　　—⟩

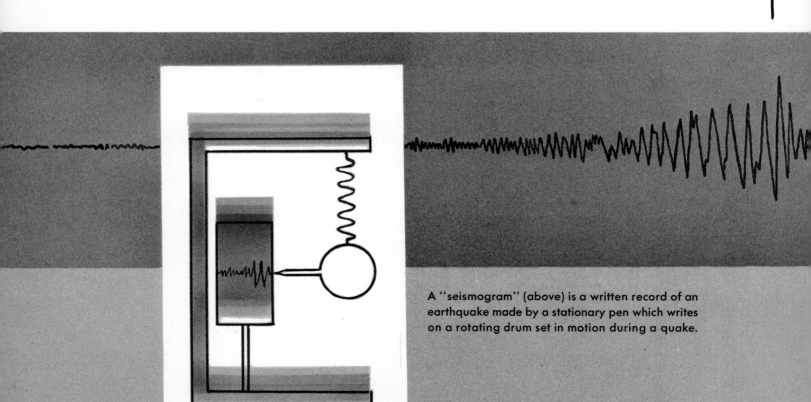

A "seismogram" (above) is a written record of an earthquake made by a stationary pen which writes on a rotating drum set in motion during a quake.

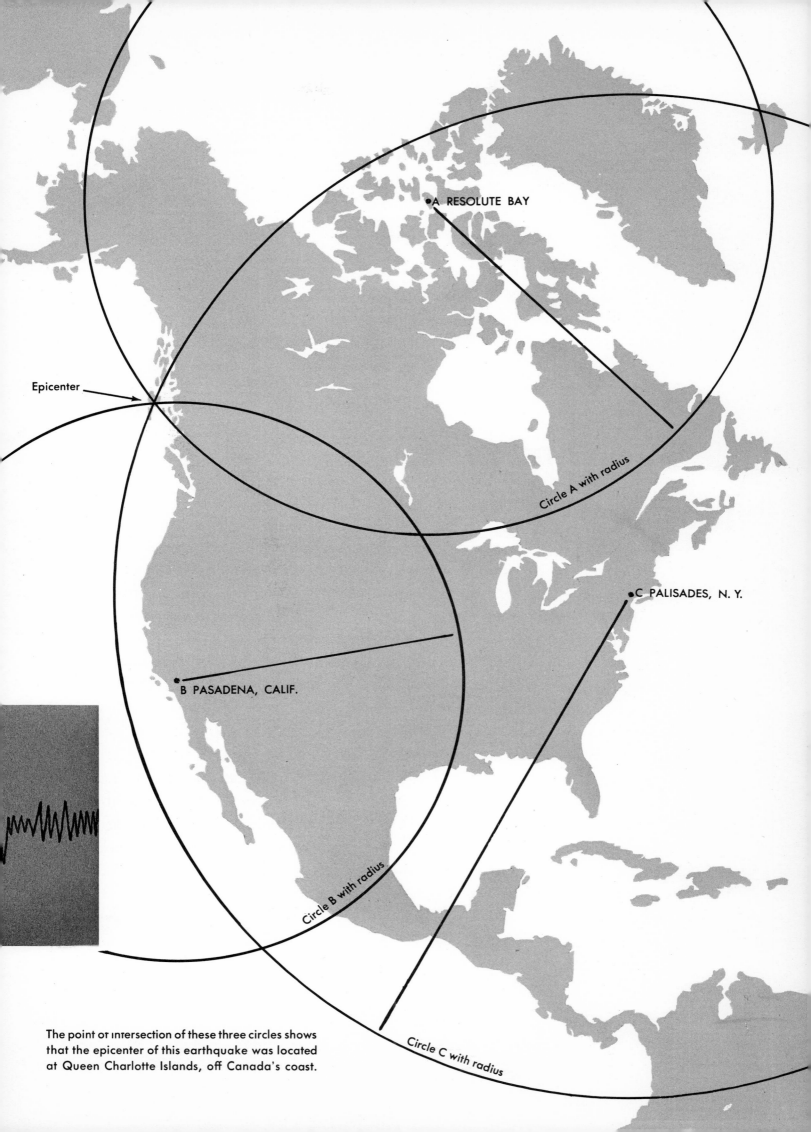

Epicenter

A RESOLUTE BAY

Circle A with radius

C PALISADES, N. Y.

B PASADENA, CALIF.

Circle B with radius

Circle C with radius

The point of intersection of these three circles shows that the epicenter of this earthquake was located at Queen Charlotte Islands, off Canada's coast.

In 1902 a hurricane of flaming gas swept down the slopes of Mt. Pelée, killing 40,000 people in the city below.

Italy's Vesuvius

volcanoes

On May 8, 1902, a few minutes before eight in the morning, forty thousand people were engulfed by a hurricane of flame that swept down the slopes of Mt. Pelée, a volcanic mountain overlooking the city of St. Pierre on the island of Martinique in the West Indies. In a matter of minutes what had once been a picturesque coastal city was reduced to charred ruins by the fury of an exploding volcano.

A month before the eruption residents of St. Pierre had noticed wisps of smoke rising lazily from the quiet mountain. Hikers climbed the slopes to investigate and returned saying that they had heard rumblings deep within the mountain. Pelée, they feared, was about to go on a rampage; but others scoffed at the idea, saying that Pelée had been sleeping for fifty-one years. The possibility of its erupting seemed remote. As the days wore on the townspeople began to hear dull explosions within the mountain. Then peaceful Pelée awoke. It began belching clouds of ash from its crater. Instinctively animals moved down from the slopes, away from the disturbance. Within a few days the island was coated with a thin film of white ash. On May 5th there were more explosions, this time followed by sprays of boiling mud and an artillery of rocks fired from the crater. At this stage many people tried to leave St. Pierre, but reports have it that the local governor posted soldiers around the town to prevent anyone from leaving; elections were only a few days away.

74

Meanwhile several ships entered the harbor, joining those resting lazily at anchor. Then on that fateful morning three days later, Pelée, like a giant flame thrower, spewed its breath of fire down the mountainside onto St. Pierre. All—save one person—were killed. The one was a prisoner locked in the protective dungeon of the local jail.

One of the ships lying off St. Pierre that Thursday morning was the *Roraima*. Assistant Purser Thompson was an eyewitness to Pelée's rampage. Here is what he saw:

" . . . Of eighteen vessels lying in, only one escaped, and she, I hear, lost more than half on board. It was a dying crew that took her out. . . . For hours before we entered the roadsted we could see flames and smoke rising from Mt. Pelée. No one on board had any idea of danger. Captain G. T. Muggah was on the bridge, and all hands got on deck to see the show. The spectacle was magnificent. As we approached St. Pierre we could distinguish the rolling and leaping of the red flames that belched from the mountain in huge volumes and gushed high in the sky. Enormous clouds of black smoke hung over the volcano. The flames were then spurting straight up in the air, now and then waving to one side or the other a moment, and again leaping suddenly higher up. There was a constant muffled roar . . . then there was a tremendous explosion about seven forty-five, soon after we got in. The mountain was blown to pieces. There was no warning. The side of the volcano was ripped out, and there hurled straight toward us a solid wall of flame. It sounded like thousands of cannon. The wave of fire was on us and over us like a lightning flash. It was like a hurricane of fire, which rolled in mass straight down upon St. Pierre and the shipping. The town vanished before our eyes, and then the air grew stifling hot and we were in the thick of it. Wherever the mass of fire struck the sea, the water boiled and sent up vast clouds of steam. I saved my life by running to my stateroom and burying myself in the bedding. The blast of fire from the volcano lasted only a few minutes. It shriveled and set fire to everything it touched. Burning rum ran in streams down every street and out into the sea. Before the volcano burst, the landings of St. Pierre were crowded with people. After the explosion not one living being was seen on land. . . ."

The fury of an erupting volcano is a terrible thing for those unfortunate enough to be nearby. In the year A.D. 79 Mount Vesuvius in southern Italy erupted after a thousand years of sleep. Early indications

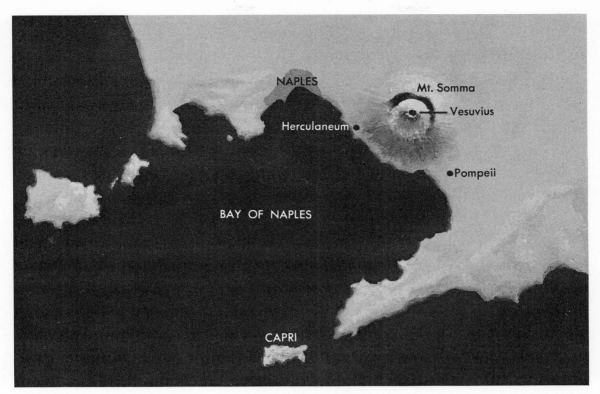

Vesuvius, on the Bay of Naples, "grows" out of the old crater of Mt. Somma. During the tragic eruption of Vesuvius in A.D. 79, the towns of Pompeii and Herculaneum were buried by pumice and a vast flood of lava.

that the mountain was awakening came in the year A.D. 63 with a series of violent earthquakes. Then around noon on August 24, 79, the mountain burst forth in a succession of terrible explosions. First came suffocating clouds of dust and hot gases, then white pumice that rained down on and completely buried the town of Pompeii on the southeast. Next a water-soaked clinker-like material welled up within the mountain, overflowed the crater rim, and rushed down the slopes in a mudflow that buried the town of Herculaneum on the southwest. Hundreds of families were buried alive by seething lava which cemented them where they were caught—some in positions of collapse, others as they attempted to flee. Not until seventeen centuries after the eruption, when the remains of devastated Pompeii were discovered, did men learn the full tragic story of Vesuvius, A.D. 79.

In 1883 the volcanic island of Krakatoa, near Java and Sumatra, blew its top in one of the greatest explosions of modern times. On August 26 the mountain island began erupting in a series of explosions, then the following day there was one mighty blast of flame, smoke, and ash. When the sea calmed and the air cleared, there was nothing. The moun-

77

tain had disappeared from the surface of the sea. At one point where the island had risen twenty-six hundred feet the sea became nine hundred feet deep. The noise from the explosion was heard seventeen hundred miles away in Australia, and a pressure wave of air traveled around the globe. The sea, churned up by the explosion, rose in a great wave that crashed down on coastal villages of Java and Sumatra killing thirty-six thousand five hundred people. For more than a year after Krakatoa blew up, ash and dust from the explosion hung in the air around the world creating bizarre conditions. Purple snowfalls and green sunsets were reported in some areas.

how volcanoes erupt

In violent volcanic eruptions you can expect a sequence of events: First, as with Mt. Pelée, there are local earthquakes around the mountain accompanied by deep-throated rumblings. Sometimes a lake associated with a volcano disappears suddenly, or changes in its level are noticed just before the mountain bursts into action. Then comes the eruption. Great blasts of steam roar out of the crater to heights of thousands of feet. During the 1779 eruption of Vesuvius, steam reportedly rose two miles above the crater.

Early in 1943, Paricutín was only a cornfield. Within a year after it first erupted it had grown to a third of the height of Vesuvius, which has been working thousands of years. An earthquake announced Paricutín.

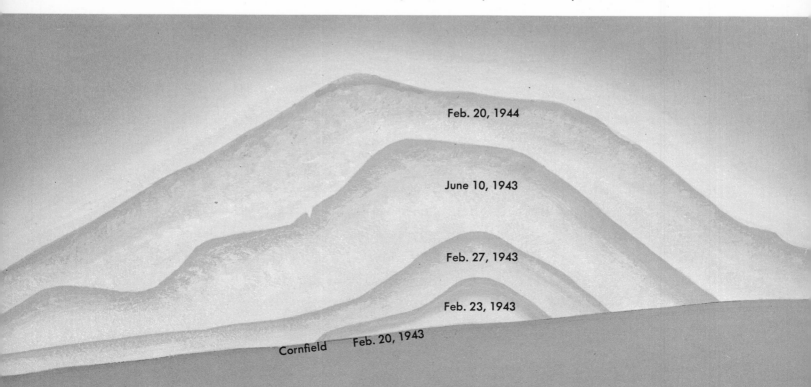

Feb. 20, 1944

June 10, 1943

Feb. 27, 1943

Feb. 23, 1943

Cornfield   Feb. 20, 1943

A thunderous roar, lightning, jets of steam, ash, rivers of lava, and lava bombs may issue from a volcano in a single eruption. Insert shows three types of bombs, called "lapilli"—bread crust, ribbon, and spindle.

Mixed with the steam are gases, rocks, dust, and ashes which are tossed and blown about this way and that. When Krakatoa blew itself to bits it sent ashes seventeen miles into the air. As the steam and other debris pour out of the crater they set up a roaring sound. When the steam rises into the upper air and cools it condenses and falls back to earth as rain. As it falls it may mix with dust and ashes and splatter to the ground in torrents of mud. Thunder and lightning boom and flash around the top of the mountain as a result of friction of the steam column against the crater walls. Eventually molten rock—magma—deep within the mountain wells up and floods over the crater walls, pouring down the mountainside in great glowing rivers of lava. Meanwhile blobs of flaming lava may be blasted out of the crater and hurled thousands of feet into the air. They solidify in spindle-shaped masses and are called volcanic bombs, or *lapilli*. Cotopaxi in Ecuador reportedly tossed a two-hundred-ton block of stone a distance of nine miles. Clouds of gases, as in the case of Mt Pelée, may pour out of the mountain in a great swelling globe of flame. No wonder men of old looked on Vesuvius, Etna, and Stromboli as entrances to the lower world of fire. In fact, the word volcano comes from the Italian *vulcano,* so named in honor of the Roman god of fire, Vulcan.

79

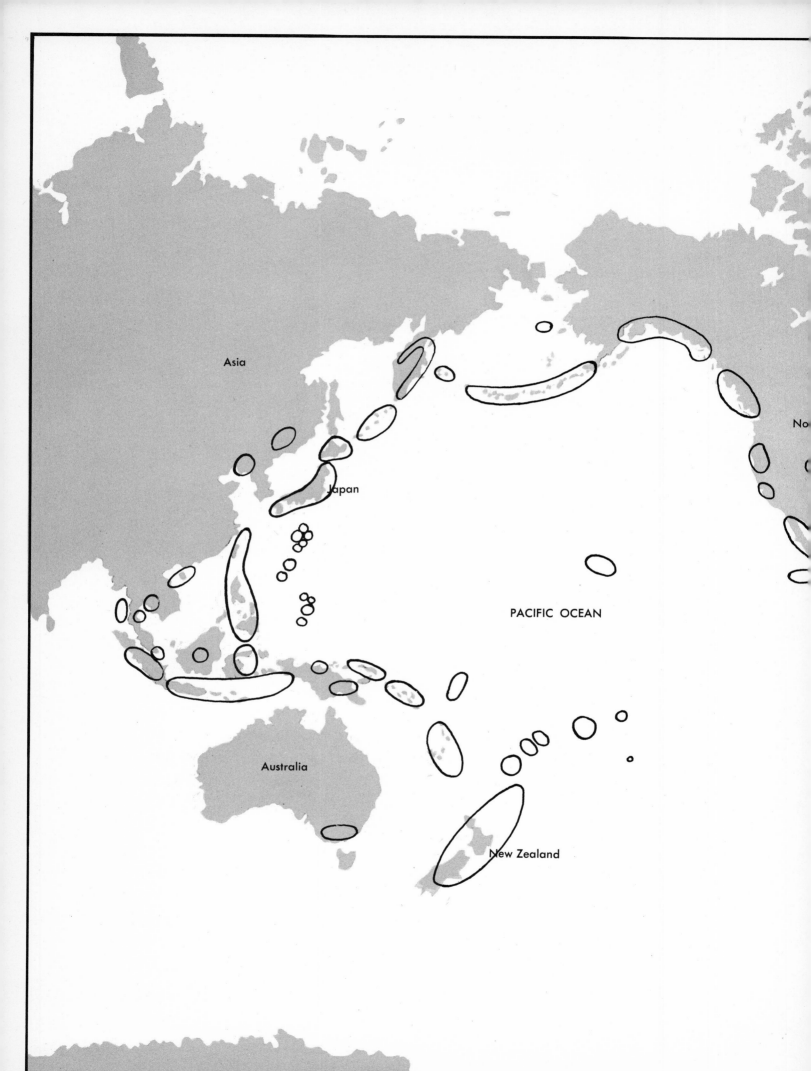

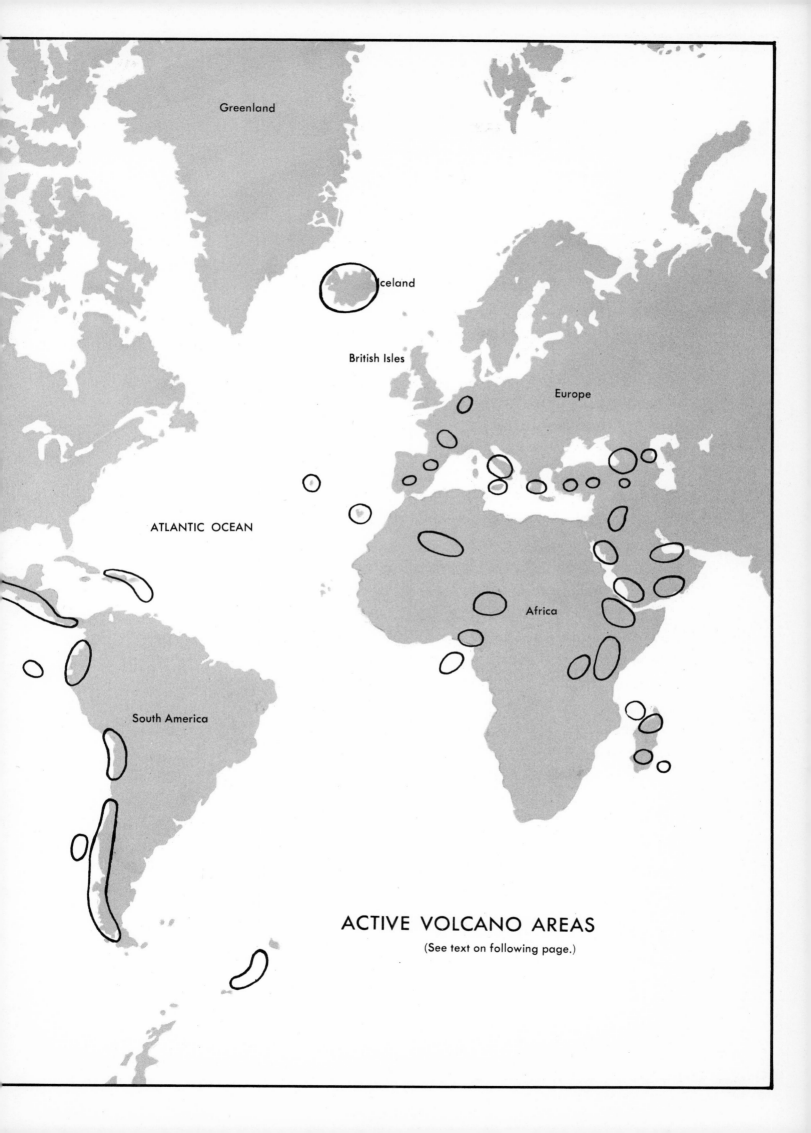

Greenland

Iceland

British Isles

Europe

ATLANTIC OCEAN

Africa

South America

ACTIVE VOLCANO AREAS

(See text on following page.)

Relatively few volcanoes put on pyrotechnic shows as spectacular as those of Mt. Pelée, Vesuvius, and Krakatoa. Such displays are rare events. There are in the world today about five hundred active volcanoes, not including many yet undiscovered beneath the seas. You can picture the world's volcanoes running along three main north-south lines. One line, about a thousand miles long, is the Mid-Atlantic Ridge (see page 33) which still has a few active volcanoes. One of these is on the island of Jan Mayen in the Greenland Sea; there are about thirteen in Iceland, six in the Azores, three in the Canaries, eight along the west coast of Africa, and six more in the West Indies. Another line of volcanoes, many of them active, extends along the eastern side of the Pacific Ocean from the Aleutians down to Cape Horn. In 1912 Katmai went on a fling, showering ash and lava over Kodiak Island. The west coast of the United States sports a few active volcanoes. Mount Hood in Oregon and Mount Rainier in Washington both give off vapor. Late in 1914 Lassen Peak in northern California erupted violently. A number of active volcanoes stretch across Mexico, among them the famous Popocatepetl which sends out puffs of smoke. Continuing south from Mexico the second line of volcanoes runs through South America, beginning with Nevado del Tolima in Colombia in the north and extending through Ecuador, Peru, and Chile in the south. The highest active volcano in the world is Cotopaxi in Ecuador. Its peak reaches to a height of 19,344 feet.

Beginning near the Bering Strait in the north, the third line of volcanoes runs along the western rim of the Pacific Ocean. On Russia's Kamchatka Peninsula are about fourteen active volcanoes. Then farther south are the Japanese islands, a long volcanic mountain chain with many active vents. This undersea belt continues through the Philippines, the Moluccas, and the Sunda Islands to New Guinea.

Volcanoes give us direct evidence of what lies deep beneath the earth's crust. Their outpourings of lava can be studied firsthand both during an eruption and later in the laboratory. One thing scientists have learned about volcanoes is that they are found in areas of young mountains. But not all young mountains have volcanoes. The Himalayas and Alps, for instance, are without volcanoes. These mountains were formed by overlappings of rock making up the earth's crust. Layer upon layer, the rocks have been pushed up to towering heights. Volcanic mountains, however, many of which are situated along fault lines, have deep fractures or cracks at their bases. From time to time these cracks serve as feeding passages through which molten rock, from tens of miles below the crust, flows to the surface. When this magma reaches the surface and flows over the land we call it lava. Some volcanoes—like Vesuvius—pour out lava in cycles of hundreds or thousands of years. Yet others are in constant eruption. Stromboli in Italy, for instance, has been ejecting lava constantly for about two thousand years. And Izalco in El Salvador has been erupting constantly since its birth in 1770.

When forces within the earth shift the rock along a volcanic fault line, pressure on the hot basalt below may be reduced. This reduced pressure allows the basalt to melt and flow upward through the fault zone as magma. Tongues of magma leading the main flow may seep into cracks cutting up through several pancake-like layers of rock called *dikes* (see diagram). Or the magma may force its way between layers of rock and remain there to form sheet-like features called *sills*. As the magma flows toward the surface the pressure on it becomes less and less. The reduced pressure allows gas trapped in the magma to bubble out of solution—just as carbon dioxide bubbles out of soda pop when you reduce the pressure by flipping off the bottle cap. The greater the escape of gas from magma, the more violent the eruption. The gases released dur-

This cross section of magma welling up from below shows a "dike" and a "sill." The lower horizontal flooding of magma, trapped between strata, forms a sill. Magma forcing its way diagonally up forms a dike.

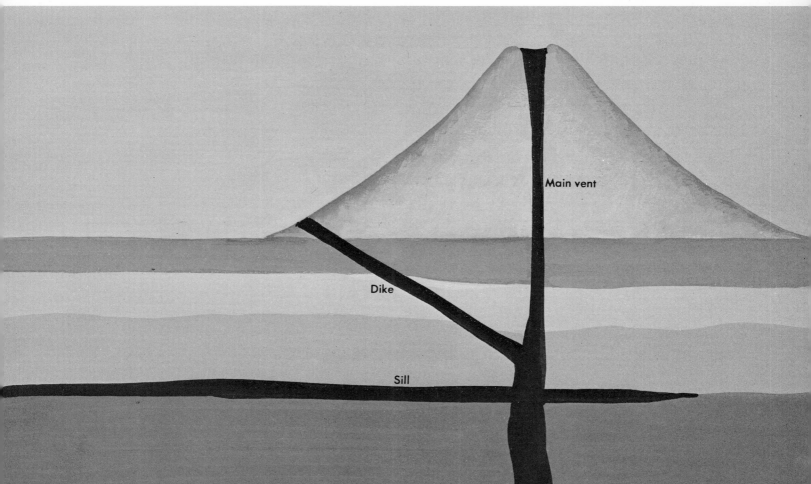

Main vent

Dike

Sill

ing an eruption are mostly water vapor and carbon dioxide; also included are sulfur dioxide, hydrogen chloride, hydrogen, and others. But the gases trapped in the magma initially are mostly hydrogen, carbon monoxide, and nitrogen. Oddly enough, the gas cloud that puffs out of a volcano is more than ninety per cent water vapor. To date geophysicists are not sure just where this water comes from: From oxygen combining with hydrogen in the magma? Or from ground water and water locked in rocks? Quite likely from both sources. As the gases escape the magma becomes more fluid, welling up to the surface more rapidly. Once a magma rise begins, and the heat within the material lasts, the magma will continue to eat its way through the earth's crust. Sometimes the process lasts millions of years.

Magma pours out of a volcano's feeding pipe as red-hot or white-hot lava about 1100°C. and flows down the mountainside in great glowing rivers, setting flame to timber and melting everything in its path. The more fluid lavas may flow overland at twenty miles an hour; the more viscous ones often proceed at a snail's pace. The viscosity, or gumminess, of magma depends on the amount of gas it holds, its temperature, and composition. Without gas, magma will not flow, nor will it explode. There are many kinds of lava between these two extreme types: 1. basalt—rich in lime, iron and magnesia; and 2. rhyolite—rich in silica and alkalies. Once exposed to the open air the lava may take years to harden, or it may harden very quickly. Some people have reported walking across beds of lava hard on the surface but still flowing red-hot below. In Mexico the volcano Jorullo erupted in 1759 with outpourings of lava; eighty-seven years later the lava was still hot enough to issue columns of steam. On the other hand, highly viscous lava may be squeezed out of a volcano like toothpaste out of a tube. The lava is so close to being solid that it freezes as a slender tower. California's Lassen Peak is a good example of such a *viscous protrusion*.

Sometimes, however, lava oozes out of long fissures or cracks in the earth. When this happens the lava spreads itself over an area of many square miles, forming a plateau instead of building a mountain. One of the most spectacular fissure lava flows known to man took place in the Pacific Northwest of the United States between ten and twenty million years ago. Geologists now know that there were a series of lava floods in this area. Intervals of quiet between flows allowed soil to form on top of one

84

lava bed and forests to grow before the next great welling-up blanketed the land. According to the University of California's Howel Williams: "Some 100,000 cubic miles of fluid lava erupted from the earth and spread over the surface; flow piled on flow until what had been a mountainous terrain was completely buried by a plateau of lava more than 5,000 feet thick and about 200,000 square miles in extent."

On June 11, 1783, in Iceland great outpourings of lava issued from the Laki fissure. Through twenty-two vents along a ten-mile line and in tongues twelve to fifteen miles wide and a hundred feet deep, the lavas came, washing over the land, drying up the Skapta River, filling in a lake, and destroying everything in their path. After the lava flow subsided the dead were counted: more than nine thousand people (some died from hunger and disease)—nearly one-fifth of Iceland's population —and 230 thousand head of cattle. The great outpourings of lava from fissure flows sometimes depress the earth's crust and form vast land basins. Gradually these basins may be filled in with water, with the result that beautiful lakes such as Taupo in New Zealand and Ilopango in El Salvador are formed.

how volcanoes build mountains

The lava flows we are chiefly concerned with in this chapter are those that build mountains. The kind of material ejected by a volcano and its rate and force of activity all determine the shape the mountain will take. Lava issuing from a new feed pipe piles up into a mound around the volcano's vent. The result is a cone with an open area at the top called the crater. Gradually ash, cinders, rock, and other materials flooded or exploded up through the vent may add to the mountain. In later stages of the volcano's growth the lavas may become more varied and more viscous. This gumminess of later lavas causes them to cling to the mountain's side and pile up around the crater rim. This is why volcanic mountains become increasingly steep near the top. The lovely Mount Fuji in Japan is in this sense perhaps the world's most perfectly shaped volcanic mountain. Its slopes are not broken by secondary cones and its crater rim has not been scarred by explosive eruptions—not in recent years, at least.

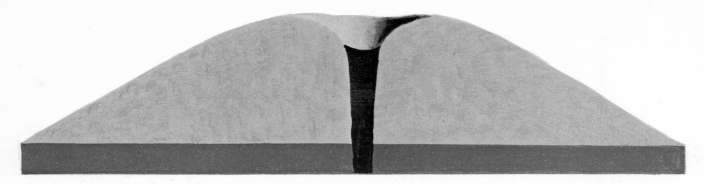

Cinder cones—are formed by great outpourings of ash and other debris. These cones build up quickly and seldom exceed a thousand feet. Lassen Volcanic National Park has such a cone.

Shield volcanoes—are built up by successive lava flows (from one or more vents) which spread out over a large flat area. Mauna Loa, in the Hawaiian Islands, is a typical shield volcano.

Calderas—are formed when the walls of a volcano collapse and tumble into the vent, leaving a great shallow basin, where there was once a peak. Oregon's Crater Lake is such a caldera.

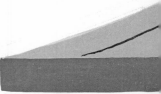

Parasitic cones—are secondary cones of a volcano. They are formed (see left slope of the mountain) when the main central vent of the volcano for some reason is sealed off.

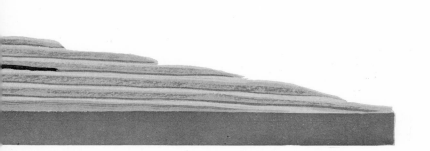

TYPES
OF
VOLCANOES

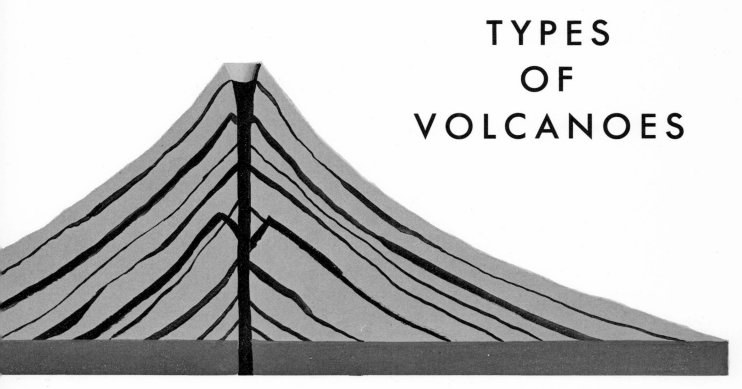

Stratovolcanoes—are built up from small mounds. Each pair of diagonal dark lines represents a lava flow. Between flows, year after year, ash and other debris are deposited. Resulting mountain is "perfectly" shaped, like Japan's famous Mt. Fuji.

Wizard Island in Crater Lake, Oregon, is a new volcano cone which has formed in the old, collapsed crater.

After a volcano has been through many cycles of erupting, the upper part of its cone may one day collapse and tumble into the crater, plugging the original vent. Such a collapsed volcano is called a *caldera*. Over the years, explosions inside the mountain weaken the walls of the vent, then in one mighty landslide the cinders, ash, and frozen lava forming the topmost part of the mountain collapse into the crater, leaving a great shallow basin where there was once a peak. Eventually the basin may become filled with water. Beautiful Crater Lake in Oregon is just such a caldera. About sixty-five hundred years ago the mountain collapsed after a series of explosions hollowed out part of the cone. Since then, however, magma has seeped up through the debris and a small new cone sticks up above the water. Tourists know the cone as Wizard Island.

A caldera does not mean that the volcano is dead. On the contrary, it may be a warning that a violent eruption is in the making. In Kilauea volcano in Hawaii lava emptied from the feed pipes deep within the mountain. This set up a series of avalanches that swept down into the crater. Ground water then rushed into the empty feed pipes and flowed into contact with deep lying magma. The result was vast quantities of steam that very quickly built up enormous pressure. In May, 1924, the mountain blew its top.

Unlike earthquakes, volcanic eruptions can be predicted fairly well. Here are three kinds of indication: 1. Seismic evidence—A series of local earthquakes around a volcano is a fairly reliable sign that the mountain is working up to an eruption. But the eruption might not come for several years. Before Vesuvius erupted in A.D. 79 earthquakes shook the area off and on for sixteen years. And before Mexico's newest volcano boiled up out of a cornfield on February 20, 1943, farmers in the area felt increasingly severe earthquakes for a period of twenty days. Deep-throated rumblings within the volcano often accompany the preliminary earthquake. 2. Ground-tilting—Before a sleeping volcano awakens into activity the ground around the mountain usually tilts this way and that. Magma welling up from below causes swellings that may change entirely the shape of a small area within several weeks. So with tiltmeters placed in choice positions around a volcano, and with a seismograph, scientists can sometimes tell about when and where an eruption will take place. The activity of Mauna Loa in Hawaii has been predicted this way. 3. Changes in magnetism—As hot non-magnetic magma wells up inside a volcano the inside walls of the mountain are heated. The combination of the magma rise and heating can produce local changes in the earth's magnetism; these changes can be detected with special instruments.

As scientists learn more about the rattlings, tiltings, and other signs a volcano gives before it strikes they are better able to warn people and so prevent disasters like those caused by Vesuvius and Pelée.

Mexico's Paricutín

Late September 1957: steam and gas clouds boil up out of the sea.

Early October 1957: a small island of lava and ash is formed.

Late October 1957: most of the new island sinks beneath the sea.

Mid-December 1957: renewed outpourings build up a new peninsula.

A VOLCANO IS BORN

Mid-September 1957 the people on the island of Fayal in the Azores felt tremors within the earth. The tremors continued for about a week. Then on September 27 clouds of steam and gases boiled up out of the sea just a few hundred yards off the island. Lava bombs were tossed half a mile into the sky and a spray of water vapor towered nearly four miles into the air. A downpour of ashes and sea spray mixed and settled over the island as salty mud, temporarily changing green lawns and fields into wastelands.

By the first week of October a new off-shore island of lava and ash had been formed after boiling its way up from the sea bottom 150 feet below. Then during the night of October 29 most of the small island, named *Ilha Nova* (new island), sank beneath the sea. But a few days later *Ilha Nova* burst forth again, only to slip away a second time the following day. On November 6 renewed activity built *Ilha Nova II*. New gases and steam announced a vigorous outpouring of ash and lava which annexed themselves to the main island, creating a half-mile-long peninsula. Diagrams show progress of the new volcano while the large illustration shows a moment during its dramatic eruption. ⟶

Mid-March 1958: still smoldering, peninsula is half mile long.

Mt. Rainier

mountains

Anyone who has gazed on the Alps, Rockies, or other majestic mountain peaks may have had the feeling that here time stands still. Here in the mountains, more than anywhere else on the land, change seems the least noticeable. From year to year we can watch streams and rivers sculpture and rebuild the lowlands; we can see the change take place within our lifetime. The mountains somehow seem permanent, indestructible, unchangeable. But they are not. As surely as the sea is ever changing the shore lines of the continents, wind, rain, and frost are sculpturing the mountains ever so slowly in a continuous process of change. Meanwhile new mountains are in the making.

In the earth's history there have been at least ten periods of crustal upheaval during which mountains have been upthrust. Some two hundred million years ago the young Appalachians, now gentle and rounded with age, were splendid snow-capped peaks, possibly as mighty as the Alps. They extended from Newfoundland to Alabama. But century after century the forces of erosion smoothed and leveled them. However, as old mountains like the Appalachians age and die, new ones are born. Today a section of the floor of the Baltic Sea is uplifting. Some geophysicists think that if it continues to rise at its present rate in a million years the uplifted section will develop into a mountain as high as Mount Everest. But *why* is this section of the sea floor rising? We do not know for certain. Possibly it is rebounding, as it has been for years, since the unloading of Pleistocene ice sheets.

We are now living in one of the periods of mountain-building. In fact, ever since man has roamed this planet he has grown up in an age of mountains. The Andes, Alps, Rockies, Himalayas—all young mountains —have buckled out of the earth's crust within the past sixty million years. About a billion years ago, in another period of mountain-making, forces within the earth caused great planet-wide upheavals. Vast outpourings of magma from within the earth, coupled with upward and downward warping, gave rise to mountain chains in some instances and formed ocean deeps in others. But by the opening of the Proterozoic era all of these mountains had been eroded away. Because the "roots" of some of these ancient peaks have been found in eastern Canada's Laurentian Hills, geologists have come to call this period of mountain-building the Laurentian Revolution. Other major mountain-building eras include the Taconic Revolution, The Appalachian Revolution, the Laramide Revolution, and the Cascadian Revolution.

how are mountains formed?

Geophysicists have long been puzzled over how mountains are formed. The birth and growth of volcanic mountains (see last chapter) are much better understood than the development of mountains that are upthrust, folded, and faulted out of the earth's crust. One reason is that volcanic mountains are sometimes born overnight and reach a height of several hundred feet in a matter of days or weeks. Scientists can watch the development of these "laboratory" mountains and so come to understand them. But mountains like the Alps, Andes, and Rockies, which are not volcanic in origin, develop over millions of years and change very slowly. Since geologic records go back only a short three hundred and fifty years or so, barely a tick of the second hand on the geologic clock, scientists have not had time to collect enough information to explain the workings of these slow-motion mountains.

Unhappily, there is no single idea that can account for mountains. According to Columbia University's Charles L. Drake, a variety of forces within the earth may join to produce mountains: expansion and contrac-

New mountains, like the towering Alps and Rockies, have sharp features not yet dulled by erosion forces.

tion of the earth's crust, heat currents within the mantle, chemical and physical changes in the materials making up the crust and mantle, movements of the crust over the mantle, and relative movements of the crust itself. While time works against the geophysicist's attempt to understand mountain-making, so does the mountain itself. Like icebergs, which poke only their heads out of the water, mountains are thought to poke only their heads above the ground. The bulk of their mass—called

94

Old mountains, like the low Appalachians, have been worn smooth by forces of erosion: wind, rain, and frost.

"roots"—extends deep into the crust. Because the geophysicist cannot see or collect samples of a mountain's roots, he cannot be sure about them. Until he learns precisely what the entire mountain is made of he will not be able to say for certain just how it came into being. Despite the annoying difficulties in understanding mountain formation, geophysicists have offered several theories which give us a glimpse of how mountains may be formed.

95

An early explanation of mountain forming held that the earth's crust is cooling and (therefore) shrinking. The result is that mountains "wrinkle" up, as the skin of a dried apple develops ridges over its surface.

A classic explanation of mountain-making is based on the idea that the earth is a shrinking planet. Picture a withering apple. As the moist pulp within the apple dries it contracts, causing the apple's skin to wrinkle and fold. Now if the earth were a cooling body it would shrink: Its skin (crust) would wrinkle and fold as the pulp (mantle and core material) contracted. The result, of course, would be mountains and valleys. According to Croneis, if in the earth's mountain-building history "the radius of our globe has decreased by a mere 200 miles, all of the ancient and modern [mountain] folding could be accounted for." So far, so good. But has the earth lost enough heat during its entire mountain-building history to account for a globe whose radius has been shortened by two hundred miles? A variety of estimates say that during the past hundred million years the earth has radiated enough heat into space to allow our planet to cool down somewhere between 10°C. and 45°C. If we take the top figure and say that the earth has cooled 45°C. in the past hundred million years, we find that this small amount of cooling would cause our planet's radius to be shortened by less than *two miles*—not the two hundred miles needed! It would seem, then, that the cooling globe idea *alone* cannot account for our planet's history of mountains. Furthermore, geophysicists are not at all sure that the earth *is* cooling; it may be growing warmer, but more about this in the section dealing with the earth's heat.

96

Another attempt to explain mountain-building comes from the idea that our planet is made up of great wedges squeezing against one another (see diagram). In the chapter about continents we described these vast land masses as "granitic rafts floating in a basalt sea." We might now imagine the continents as lightweight granitic wedges squeezed between denser wedges of basaltic material making up the sea floors. Because the basaltic wedges are denser, they tend to sink deeper toward the earth's center. As this happens they press against the sides of the continental wedges, forcing them upward, as an icicle is forced upward when you press it between your hands. The more forceful the sinking of the basaltic wedges, the more pressure there is along the sides of a continental wedge. When the stresses become great enough the top surface of the continental wedge wrinkles—the result being rocks that are folded and raised into mountain ranges. According to this theory of mountain-making, the wedges may remain at rest for many years. But eventually because of change within the earth they become active. Slowly, over thousands of years a continent-wedge is squeezed higher and higher and mountains wrinkle up along its crustal belts of weakness (mainly along the rim of the continent). No geophysicist supposes that this is the only way folded mountains are formed. However, the wedge theory may explain, in part at least, the causes of mountain-making.

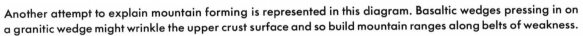

Another attempt to explain mountain forming is represented in this diagram. Basaltic wedges pressing in on a granitic wedge might wrinkle the upper crust surface and so build mountain ranges along belts of weakness.

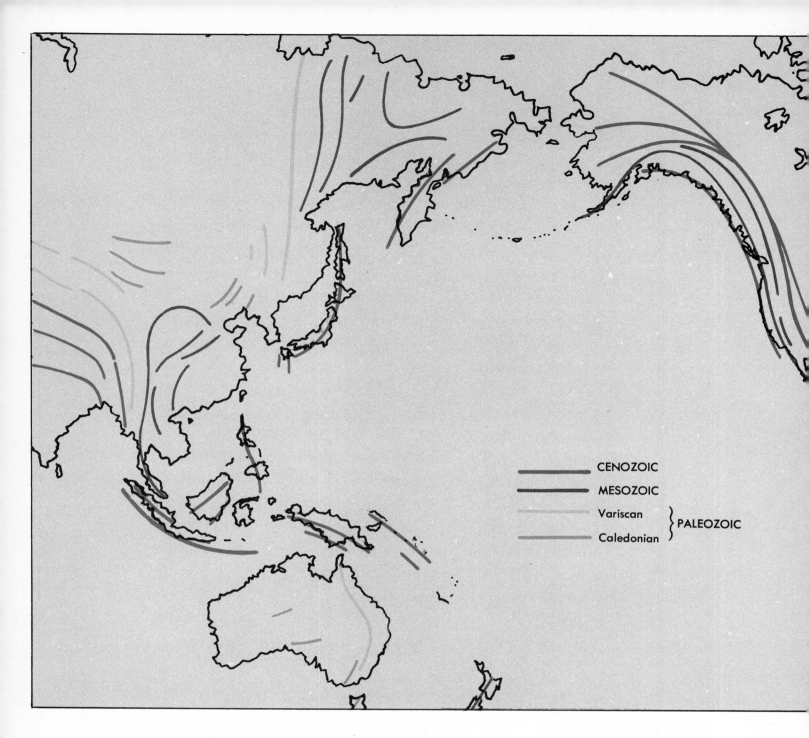

World map shows distribution of the world's folded mountains, formed when weak sedimentary rock has

CENOZOIC

MESOZOIC

Variscan

Caledonian

PALEOZOIC

In 1889 the American geologist Clarence Dutton proposed the word *isostasy* to account for mountain building, but the basic idea had been advanced earlier by James Hall. Isostasy takes us back to our description of a mountain as a "rockberg" floating within the earth's crust. In other words, a mountain may be regarded as a lightweight rock floating in a sea of heavier fluid rock, rather than a flat-bottomed rock resting on the earth's surface. Dutton knew that in the western United States there were mountain ranges rising out of vast land platforms up to sixty miles wide and two hundred miles long. He also knew that some of these

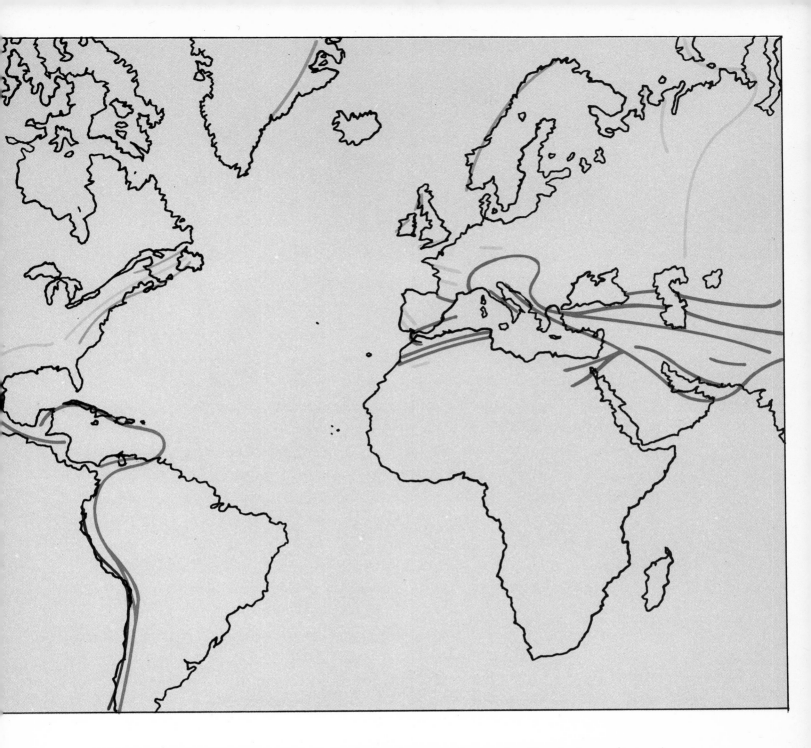

been thrust up by wrinkling of the earth's crust. Color key shows age of mountains. (See chart on endpapers.)

mountains had been worn down by erosion over the years. If all the washed-away material could be returned to the mountains, Dutton said, some of the mountains would now be about ten miles high. Yet Dutton doubted that the mountains had ever been much higher than they were when he studied them. The best explanation that could be offered was that as certain mountains are smoothed by wind and rain, and their sediments are washed down the slopes, their loss of weight somehow causes the mountain to rise up out of the plastic flow below.

The reasoning is simply this: The washed-down sediments settle on

99

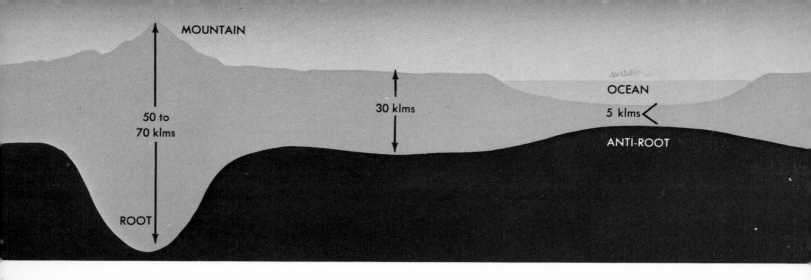

MOUNTAIN

50 to
70 klms

30 klms

OCEAN

5 klms

ANTI-ROOT

ROOT

As a mountain is worn away by erosion, it exerts less and less pressure on the basaltic material beneath. This reduced pressure allows basaltic material beneath mountain root to rise, elevating the material above.

the surrounding lowlands and so add weight to the lowlands. At the same time the mountain's weight is made less. The plastic flow material directly beneath the mountain and surrounding lowland now rearranges itself. The increased weight of sediments pressing down on the lowlands forces some of the plastic flow material below to move to an area of less pressure—under the mountain which is becoming lighter and lighter by erosion. As more and more plastic flow material pushes under the mountain's roots it lifts the mountain. The faster the process of erosion, the faster the rate of rise of the mountain. Here is where Dutton's word "isostasy," which means "equal standing," came in. In short, it seems that over our globe nature maintains a kind of balance between highland and lowland.

Another attempt to account for mountains comes under the heading of "periodic melting." The idea behind this theory tells us that some of the heat coming from radioactivity within the earth's crust is stored up in the material just beneath the crust. After enough heat has accumulated over a long period of time the temperature of the subcrust rocks nears the melting point. This high heat causes the rocks to expand horizontally. The result is upthrusted crustal rock which may fold into mountains. In many cases igneous (once-molten) rocks rather than sedimentary rocks are found at the core of folded mountains. This observation of igneous rocks which have boiled up to the surface tends to support the theory of periodic melting. But again, this theory alone cannot account for *all* mountain-building activity.

mountains from ditches

The beginning student of geology is often surprised to learn that the great mountains of the world are made up largely of sedimentary rocks, that is rocks that have been formed from sand, gravel, and other materials washed into the seas millions of years ago. Embedded in these sedimentary rocks are fossils of sea creatures that lived long before the mountains rose out of the ancient seas. High in the Alps, for instance, geologists have found the remains of countless forms of sea life. How, you may wonder, are mountains uplifted from the deep sea floors?

From time to time in geologic history great troughs called *geosynclines* develop in the earth's crust. At one time a great U-shaped geosyncline looped down through North America. One arm ran from northern Alaska down to Mexico on the Pacific coast, and the other ran from northeastern Canada down to Alabama on the Atlantic coast. At the time this great ditch existed, a vast but shallow inland sea covered most of Canada and the United States. It extended from Newfoundland to the Gulf of Mexico. For nearly three hundred million years rivers and streams washed sediments into the sea. Slowly the sea floor sank, assisted by the accumulated weight of the sediments. Meanwhile sediments filtered down into the geosyncline ditch. Eon after eon the sediments collected in the ditch, their weight causing the ditch to sink inch by inch, deeper and deeper into the earth's crust. Because the sinking kept pace with the collection of sediments, the surface of the geosyncline remained very near the level of the inland sea, sometimes above it and other times below it. Geophysicists now think that the Appalachian arm of the geosyncline sank with accumulated sediments to a depth of seven miles or so. Other geosyncline dump heaps are thought to have reached depths up to twenty miles!

Age after age, as sediments flow into a geosyncline, the great ditch slowly sinks into the crust. Then at one point in time something else begins to happen. Lateral pressures become strong enough to squeeze the sediments deep into the earth and at the same time thrust them up

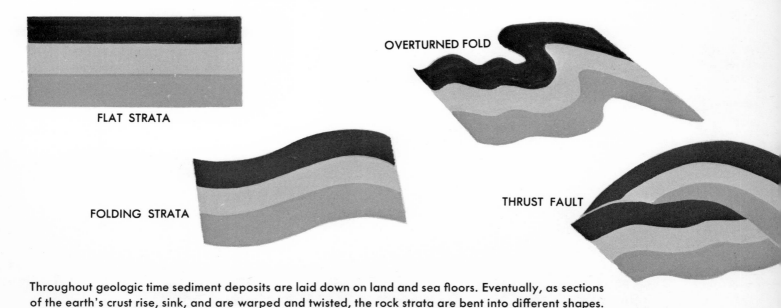

FLAT STRATA

FOLDING STRATA

OVERTURNED FOLD

THRUST FAULT

Throughout geologic time sediment deposits are laid down on land and sea floors. Eventually, as sections of the earth's crust rise, sink, and are warped and twisted, the rock strata are bent into different shapes.

Volcanic mountain

FAMILY OF MOUNTAINS

Mountains are formed in different ways. VOLCANIC
MOUNTAINS are formed when molten rock from the earth's
interior boils up, or heaps up cinders and ashes into a cone.
FOLDED MOUNTAINS are formed when weak sedimentary
rock is thrust up by wrinkling of the earth's crust. RESIDUAL
MOUNTAINS are the result of great uprisings of land becoming a plateau which is etched and carved by water
draining off it, the softer parts being washed away first.
BLOCK MOUNTAINS are formed when the earth's crust
slips vertically along a long crack, one side rising and the
other sinking. Eventually rain and wind wear the sharp
edges smooth.

Residual mountains

Folded mountains

Block mountains

Upheavals of land sometimes squeeze rock strata into a series of humps (anticlines) and dips (synclines). The humps become mountains, the dips become valleys.

toward the sky. The result may be a mountain chain, such as the Appalachians and the Rockies. Both the Appalachians and the Rockies, then, began as geosyncline ditches which millions of years of sediment accumulation filled in and depressed. During the long period of sediment accumulation sea creatures died, filtered down, and mingled with the layers of sediments. Eventually the sediments were thrust downward and upward and so became new mountains.

Mountain-building by sediment-filled ditches folding upward most likely goes on continuously in one part of the world or another. According to Drake, today there are two sedimentary troughs off the east coast of North America north of Cape Hatteras. "The inner trough, under the continental shelf, contains sediments up to 17,000 feet in thickness," Drake says, and "the other trough, under the continental slope and rise, contains a greater thickness of sediments, up to 30,000 feet off the Grand Banks of Newfoundland." Are these two ditches approaching the stage when they will one day thrust up and fold into new mountains which will add to the land area along the northeast coast of North America? Possibly, but we know all too little about the sources of energy that touch off mountain-building of this type. And until we learn more we will have to be content with educated guesswork.

classes of mountains

Folded mountains—The largest mountain systems of the world are folded mountains. They are made up of thick sedimentary rocks which years ago were upthrust by the crust which squeezed weaker sedimentary materials up into folds. The folding process leaves two kinds of features: 1. the up-arches which are called *anticlines;* and 2. the depressions between anticlines called *synclines.* Switzerland's Jura Mountains are an example of the anticline-syncline system of folded mountains. The Appalachians, Rockies, and the Sierra Nevadas are all mountains produced by the folding process.

Fault mountains—Sometimes great breaks occur in the earth's crust. When this happens the ground on one side of the break may slip down hundreds of feet, while the ground on the other side of the break remains stable. The result is a solid rock wall which may be hundreds of feet high. When the slippage is great enough a block or fault mountain is produced. Eventually rain and wind erode the sharp edge of the block leaving a conventional rounded-top mountain. Utah, Nevada, and Arizona have several fault mountains of this type.

Volcanic mountains—As we discovered in earlier sections, molten rock sometimes flows up through long cracks in the earth's crust and builds into mountain chains. Also, isolated mountains like Fuji, Shasta, and Hood are the result of volcanic action. Outpourings of lava, cinders, ash, and other materials through a feed pipe pile up over the years and build these isolated mountains. (See section about volcanoes.)

Residual mountains—Sometimes great flat areas of land rise up above the surrounding plain, rather than fold up into mountains. The result is a plateau. After many years, water draining off the plateau cuts into and eats away the softer earth and rock. At first only shallow ridges of hard rock are left exposed, but over the years these ridges tower higher and higher as the softer parts of the plateau are etched away. The Allegheny plateau is a region with mountains of the residual type.

While we can observe, study, and describe various kinds of mountains simply by walking over the earth's surface, this does not tell us the "inside story" of mountains, so to speak. In other words, that part of a mountain which we cannot examine by direct means we must examine by indirect means—by using seismic waves, gravity, and heat measurements, to mention only three. In a sense this is like groping in the dark and trying to describe an object only on the basis of what your fingers tell you about the object. This is the problem the geophysicist faces when he goes exploring under the earth. In the last sections of this book we will deal with these probings in the dark and in the process we will find ourselves at the frontiers of present-day geophysics.

Mt. Hood

105

GLACIERS ON THE MOVE

From time to time in the earth's history great walls of ice two miles high have bulldozed their way over one third of our planet. As the ice advanced it upturned hills and dug valleys. The last glacier also depressed great holes in the land; then when the ice melted the holes became placid lakes. The Greak Lakes and hundreds of smaller ones in northeastern United States and Canada are the work of glaciers on the move. We are still at the tail end of the last ice age. Barely 10,000 years ago Lake Michigan and Lake Huron were half filled with glacier ice.

The last ice age began about a million years ago. Scientists think that four times during this epoch ice sheets crept down over parts of North America, then receded. As recently as 24,600 years ago the ice marched down from the Arctic, invading Ohio, Indiana, and Illinois. Great trees were snapped like matchsticks and the soil was upturned as if it were a vast garden. Then 18,000 years ago a warmer climate began to melt the glacier. But during the melting the climate turned cold again, twice allowing the glacier to advance farther south. Each time it bull-

dozed forests into the earth, the second time reaching as far south as Michigan and Wisconsin. This was about 10,700 years ago. Today the remains of the last glacial ice are found in Greenland and parts of Ellesmere and Baffin islands.

What causes the march of glaciers is pretty much of a puzzle. Some scientists look to chemical changes in the air, or volcanic dust and ashes which hang in the upper atmosphere and block out part of the sun's rays for long periods of time. Or possibly the sun itself is a cause. If solar radiation weakens from time to time a deep cold could grip the planet and allow the advance of glaciers.

Columbia's Maurice Ewing and William Donn believe that we may be headed for another ice age. The melting of the Arctic ice may touch it off, they believe. As the Arctic ice remaining from the last glacier continues to melt, it produces more and more moisture in northern areas. Eventully, as the quantity of moisture increases, great snows will fall and will last throughout each year. Slowly the snows will add to the remaining glaciers in the north, and when the glaciers reach towering heights they will begin to creep down over North America and Europe. ⟶⟩

Modern boat
compass

the earth as a magnet

For many years scientists have known that our planet is a giant magnet. Like a simple bar magnet, the earth has north and south magnetic poles that direct the motion of compass needles. The north pole needle end of a compass will always line up with the earth's north magnetic pole (providing there is no outside disturbing influence such as electric storms on the sun). While scientists have known for years that the earth is a magnet, they have not been able to explain the hows and whys of its magnetism. Again, as we found in earlier chapters, many of the earth's secrets are locked inside our globe; and until we invent new scientific instruments which can probe into the mantle and core we will have to be content with bits and pieces of knowledge.

History books generally give the Chinese credit for first discovering the magnet. Just how and when they made the discovery we do not know. Some authorities say twenty-five hundred years before the birth of Christ, but one of the earliest Chinese documents describing magnetism dates much later—in the third century A.D. The document reveals only that a needle enables a ship to steer in a southward direction. In the late 1200's Petrus de Maricourt, a soldier-monk, described the action of a compass needle in these words: "Take a loadstone and put it in a wooden cup or plate and set it afloat, like a sailor in a boat, upon water in a large vessel where it will have room to turn. Then the stone so placed

108

When compasses came into popular use for navigation, no one understood exactly why the needle pointed.

in the boat will turn until the north pole of the stone will come to rest in the direction of the north pole of the heavens, and its south pole toward the south pole of the heavens. And if you move the stone from that position a thousand times, a thousand times will it return by the will of God."

For the next four hundred years, although the compass was used widely for sea navigation, no one understood *why* the needle always pointed in the same direction. During this period scientists and navigators alike supposed that some force beyond the earth controlled the compass needle, a physical force within the stars (the Pole Star was a favorite), or a spiritual force in the heavens.

Today we know that the earth's magnetism, which makes compass needles behave the way they do, has its roots deep within our globe, not somewhere in the heavens. But just what that force is remains somewhat of a mystery. For one thing, we cannot probe within the earth to find out what forces are at work there; and for another, the earth's magnetism seems to be in constant change. Sailors and fliers have long known that navigation charts showing regional variations in the earth's magnetism have to be brought up to date every few years. At one time and place a navigator's compass needle will point a few degrees west of true north;

109

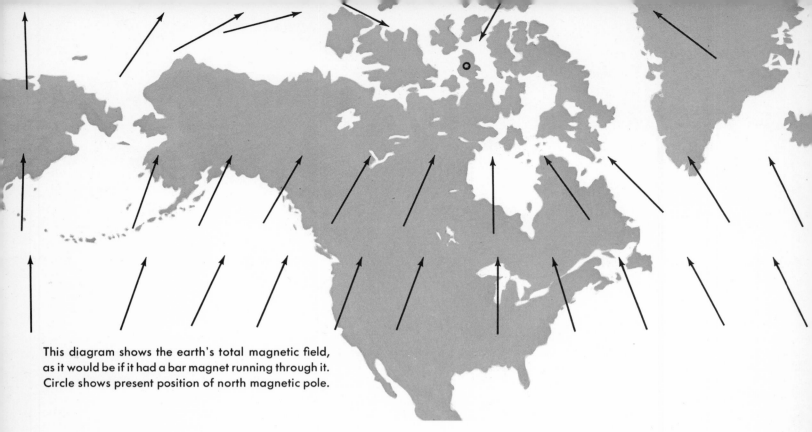

This diagram shows the earth's total magnetic field, as it would be if it had a bar magnet running through it. Circle shows present position of north magnetic pole.

but when the navigator returns to the same place several years later he may be surprised to find that his needle now points a few degrees *east* of true north. At the same time that the earth's magnetic field changes direction in a given region, its strength may change pace. Lines of force that have been weak for several years in a particular region may gradually become stronger over a period of fifteen years or so.

The over-all strength, as well as regional strengths, of the earth's magnetic field also changes. In the last hundred years or so scientists have found that the strength of the earth's over-all field has fallen off about five per cent. If this rate should continue, in another two thousand years or so the magnetic compass would become useless as a navigation instrument. But there seems to be no need to worry. According to the University of California's Walter M. Elsasser, "There is evidence that in the last few years the decline in strength has begun to slow down, and the trend may turn upward in the near future."

In addition to the changes mentioned so far, the earth's magnetic personality changes in still other ways. For example, the north magnetic pole of our planet is a wanderer. Throughout geologic time it has been weaving about the Arctic, as the diagram shows. At the present time it seems to be settled just north of Canada near the 70th latitude, which places it about a thousand miles from the true North Pole. Not only does the north magnetic pole wander, but many geophysicists suspect that in past ages the north and south magnetic poles have changed places—not once, but quite possibly several times.

110

THE WANDERING POLES

TEN-YEAR PERIOD ENDING	POSITION OF NORTH MAGNETIC POLE	POSITION OF SOUTH MAGNETIC POLE
1912	71°N., 97°W.	71°S., 150.5°E.
1922	71°N., 97°W.	70°S., 149°E.
1932	72°N., 98°W.	69°S., 148°E.
1942	73°N., 98°W.	68°S., 146°E.

The above figures are based on reports from the Carnegie Institution.

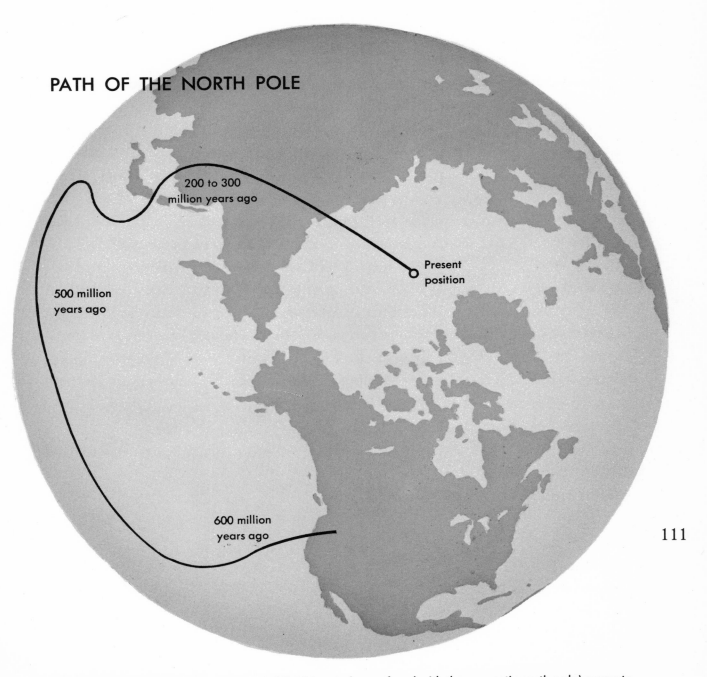

PATH OF THE NORTH POLE

200 to 300 million years ago

500 million years ago

Present position

600 million years ago

The North Pole of the earth's main axial field (not to be confused with the magnetic north pole) seems to have moved about throughout geologic time. The wavy line on the globe roughly traces the wandering Pole.

These polar puzzlers are not easy to figure out, nor is the major question underlying all studies of the earth's magnetism, namely: *What are the forces within our planet that make the earth a magnet?* Let's backtrack for a moment and briefly review the work of the brilliant English scientist William Gilbert, who has been called the "Galileo of magnetism," then look at some present-day theories that attempt to account for the earth's magnetism.

In 1600 Gilbert published *De Magnete,* a book that excited the scientific community of his day. In it he said that the earth is a giant magnet which influences compass needles, and that the Pole Star has nothing to do with a compass needle's pointing north. He also made it clear that a line drawn from true north to true south formed the axis about which the earth rotates. Furthermore, this axis of rotation, he said, should not be confused with the axis resulting from a line connecting the magnetic north and magnetic south poles. The two north and two south polar points are quite different, he maintained. Gilbert's major contribution at this stage, however, was his tracing of the earth's magnetic field. He began his experiments by cutting a piece of naturally magnetized mineral called "loadstone" into a sphere shaped like the earth. Then by moving small magnetic needles over his loadstone sphere he was able to trace the loadstone's lines of force. His conclusion was a simple one: Like the loadstone, the earth is a magnet with similar lines of force. But what makes it a magnet? Gilbert suspected that the earth's over-all magnetic field was produced by a large and permanent magnetic body within the earth. However, as soon as later scientists learned that the earth's deep interior is terribly hot, Gilbert's idea of a permanent magnetic body was given up. Any magnet heated to the temperature of the earth's deep interior quickly loses its magnetism. Nevertheless, Gilbert's contribution was an outstanding one. Before his experiments were published no one understood the nature of the earth's magnetic field of force.

two kinds of magnetism

112

Gilbert's experiments dealt with what geophysicists today call the earth's *primary* magnetism. But even before Gilbert published *De Magnete* experimenters knew of secondary or *residual* magnetic forces, which inter-

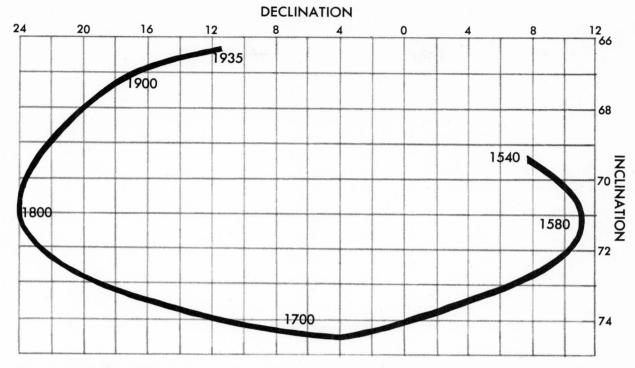

DECLINATION

Diagram shows the path "traced" by an imaginary compass needle free to swing from side to side and up and down, from a period from 1540 through 1935. Path indicates westward wandering of the magnetic pole.

fere with the earth's primary field. In the year 1580, for instance, observations made in London showed that the compass needle pointed 11° east of true north. But during the years up to 1812 the needle for some reason reversed its swing and pointed 24° west of true north. Ever since that time the needle has been gradually shifting back toward the east. Today it points about only 10° west of true north. For years scientists have attempted to predict or work out a cycle for these secondary changes, but to date they have had little luck. One reason is that a scant four hundred years of measurements in only a few locations are hardly enough to go on. If they had records going back a few thousand years, and made at properly selected recording stations around the globe, they would be much better off. Also, without an understanding of what forces within the earth produce these secondary changes they are greatly handicapped. Scientists, however, do have some clews about the residual magnetic field. According to the British geophysicist S. K. Runcorn, the residual field seems to be working its way around the globe in a westward direction. "The residual field," he says, "may be likened to a formation of moving clouds: It is continually changing in form and also drifting as a whole. The drift has been steadily westward throughout the centuries of observation. At the rate it has been moving, the residual field would travel full circle around the earth in about 1600 years."

113

what magnetized our planet?

Of all the theories attempting to account for the earth's magnetism none can be accepted as the final answer. Some geophysicists feel that the material forming the earth's central core, or possibly the material immediately surrounding the core, is capable of being magnetized. One objection to this theory, however, takes us back to Gilbert; namely, that the high temperatures in and around the core would discourage magnetization. But would they? Some physicists have suggested that the extremely high pressures found at core depths within the earth may offset the high-temperature effects. This could mean that magnetizable material may exist there. Unhappily this idea cannot be proved or disproved because we cannot produce as high pressures in the laboratory as nature produces within the earth.

Another attempt to explain the earth's magnetic field comes from Elsasser. In brief, he says that the flow of molten iron-nickel material making up the earth's core generates electric currents. These currents in turn set up the primary magnetic field invisibly lacing the globe. Elsasser explains his "dynamo" theory by comparing our earth-dynamo with Michael Faraday's simple disk dynamo.

Faraday's dynamo consists of nothing more than a copper disk (see diagram) that spins above a bar magnet placed just under the edge of the disk. As the spinning disk passes through the field of the magnet a small current is set up in the disk. By spinning the disk continuously we can keep a current flowing, as shown in the diagram. This, then, is the dynamo principle: Mechanical energy (spinning of the disk) is changed into electrical energy (current).

Now let's look at our planet as a dynamo, as Elsasser sees it. He says that the earth's core is just the kind of medium a Faraday-type dynamo requires. It is made of an iron-nickel alloy, which is a good conductor of electricity; and since it is a liquid, matter can move about within it. In short, "it allows both mechanical motion and the flow of current, and the interaction of these can generate self-sustaining currents and magnetism," says Elsasser. He feels that the core material must be in constant motion. If it were not, he argues, then why do we notice changes in the earth's magnetic field? If the core were stable and motionless the magnetic field would probably remain steady.

114

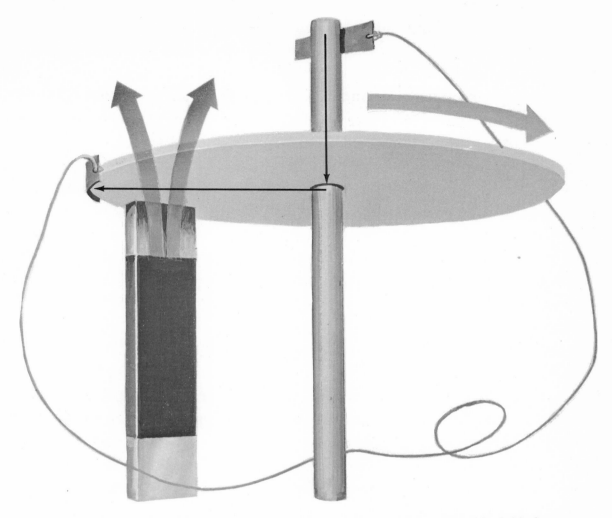

Faraday proved that an electric current could be set up by spinning a copper disk in the field of a magnet. (See text opposite.) Elsasser has suggested that the earth's magnetic field may result from such a dynamo.

By measuring the changes in the field Elsasser says that we can work out the speed of moving particles within the core: The figure comes out to about a hundredth of an inch a second. Not very fast for a dynamo, you may be thinking. But Elsasser says that it is fast enough, because theory shows that the larger a dynamo is the slower it needs to turn in order to produce a flow of current.

So far, so good. But what causes these motions within the core? One answer is heat flowing outward from the core. This would set up convection currents similar to those you see in a pan of boiling water. Another possible answer is this: Differences in chemical make-up within the core could cause the core's material to move about. This happens in the oceans when the salt content of neighboring patches of water differs. Whatever causes the motion, Elsasser says, many electric currents in the form of eddies are set up within the core, and the eddies are constantly changing as particle movement within the core changes.

So far in Elsasser's argument we can account for only local currents —not the earth's over-all magnetic field. What, then, produces the more or less stable primary magnetic field with its lines of force looping from pole to pole, as if a great bar magnet were inside our globe? Elsasser thinks that in some way the earth's rotation lines up the various local eddies and so produces the primary field. If not, he asks, why is the primary field aligned with the earth's axis of rotation? As with so many other theories in science time and untold man-hours of research will be the final judge of Elsasser's dynamo theory.

reversing poles?

Riddles about the earth's magnetism seem endless. One that puzzles scientists today is the suggestion that our planet's magnetic poles have flip-flopped, or reversed positions, many times in the past. Runcorn, who has studied the reversing pole idea, says that natural compass needles frozen into rocks through the ages leave permanent records of at least part of the earth's magnetic history.

These compass needles are grains of magnetized iron. When a volcano erupts and pours lava over the surrounding area the iron grains contained in the lava become magnetized. This happens because the atoms making up the hot iron are eager to line up along any magnetic field. So as the lava pours over the surrounding countryside the hot iron grains are magnetized and line up along the local magnetic field. Gradually they "freeze" in this position and become permanent markers that show the direction of magnetic lines of force in the area. These magnetic fossils, then, show scientists the direction of the earth's field when the igneous rock was formed. According to Runcorn, in Iceland, the northwest United States, and other parts of the world there are layers upon layers of lava flows, each containing millions of these natural compass needles which, chapter by chapter, reveal the earth's magnetic history. Like nearly every other promising theory in geophysics this one, too, has its shortcomings. Some leading geophysicists, for example, do not accept this idea because they

116

don't know just what effect several layers of lava packed on top of one another might have on the alignment of the iron grains.

Runcorn tells us that these natural compass needles are also found in fine-grained sedimentary rocks. "After magnetized particles were eroded from old volcanic rock," he says, "they would tend to line up along the earth's field when they settled in sediments. Then when the beds hardened into rock, the magnetic particles would be fixed in the direction of the field at the time." Runcorn and others have studied these magnetic records in sedimentary rocks at various places around the world. And what they have come up with has baffled many scientists. The records clearly show that between sixty million and one million years ago the geomagnetic poles have reversed places many times. But how? Could it be that from time to time the primary magnetic field of the earth dies out, or breaks up, then forms again with opposite polarity? To date no one can answer the question. Some geophysicists who are skeptical of the reversing pole idea think that the natural compass needles themselves in some way reversed their magnetic directions rather than that the earth reversed its direction. Even so, says Runcorn, "the more rocks and locations we examine, the more the evidence accumulates that the earth did reverse its field many times."

Like hundreds of other scientific puzzles associated with the earth, this one probably will not be solved during our lifetime. And why should it be? After all, our planet is some four and a half billion years old, but man has been around for only a million years or so. And during only a pitifully small part of this time has he had the tools and intelligence with which to explore this planet scientifically.

Earth's magnetic field

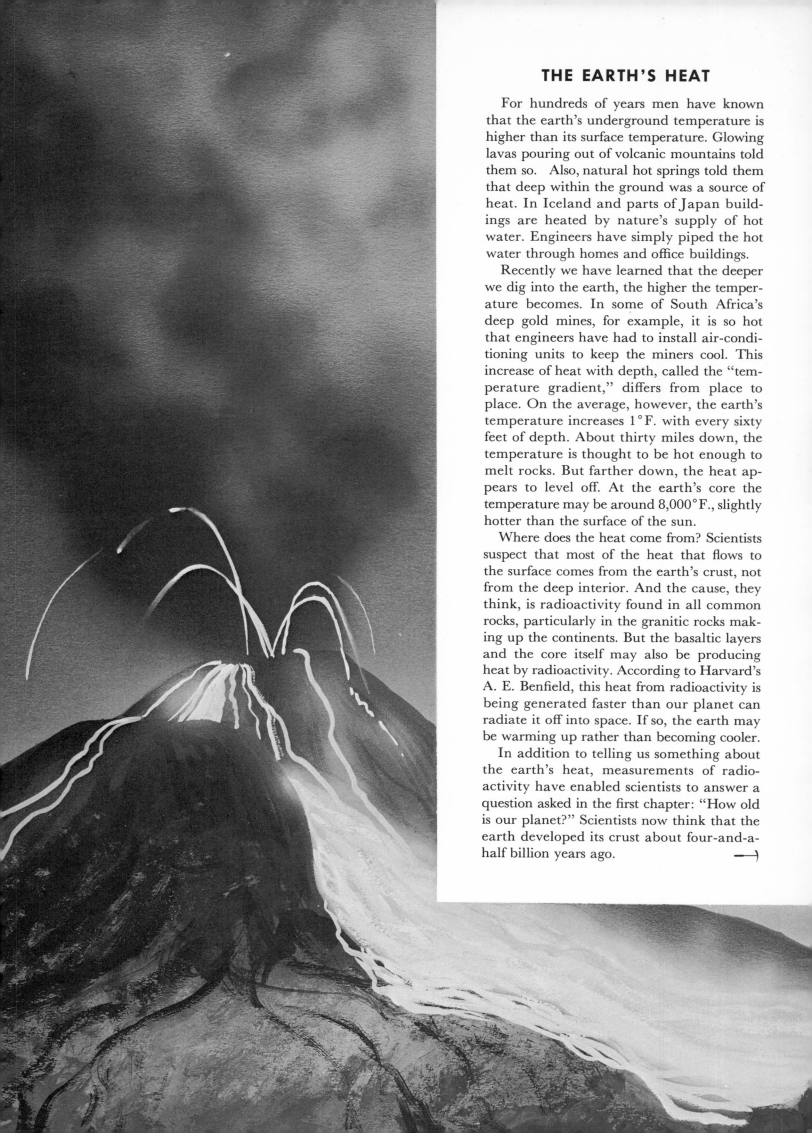

THE EARTH'S HEAT

For hundreds of years men have known that the earth's underground temperature is higher than its surface temperature. Glowing lavas pouring out of volcanic mountains told them so. Also, natural hot springs told them that deep within the ground was a source of heat. In Iceland and parts of Japan buildings are heated by nature's supply of hot water. Engineers have simply piped the hot water through homes and office buildings.

Recently we have learned that the deeper we dig into the earth, the higher the temperature becomes. In some of South Africa's deep gold mines, for example, it is so hot that engineers have had to install air-conditioning units to keep the miners cool. This increase of heat with depth, called the "temperature gradient," differs from place to place. On the average, however, the earth's temperature increases 1°F. with every sixty feet of depth. About thirty miles down, the temperature is thought to be hot enough to melt rocks. But farther down, the heat appears to level off. At the earth's core the temperature may be around 8,000°F., slightly hotter than the surface of the sun.

Where does the heat come from? Scientists suspect that most of the heat that flows to the surface comes from the earth's crust, not from the deep interior. And the cause, they think, is radioactivity found in all common rocks, particularly in the granitic rocks making up the continents. But the basaltic layers and the core itself may also be producing heat by radioactivity. According to Harvard's A. E. Benfield, this heat from radioactivity is being generated faster than our planet can radiate it off into space. If so, the earth may be warming up rather than becoming cooler.

In addition to telling us something about the earth's heat, measurements of radioactivity have enabled scientists to answer a question asked in the first chapter: "How old is our planet?" Scientists now think that the earth developed its crust about four-and-a-half billion years ago.

When water trapped within the earth's crust comes in contact with hot rock, steam is produced. Sometimes this steam hisses and roars to the surface through natural vents. Such steam wells are found on New Zealand's North Island. By sinking pipes into the hot region below, engineers can trap the steam and make it drive turbines, which in turn generate electricity. Steam wells in central Italy have been used to drive power plants since 1913. California's engineers have also tapped this age-old source of natural power.

Right: Old Faithful, in Yellowstone National Park, erupts once an hour in spurts lasting for about five minutes. During each eruption it sends 10,000 to 12,000 gallons of water up to 150 feet in the air.

FACTS ABOUT THE EARTH

Equatorial diameter	7926.28 mi.
Polar diameter	7899.98 mi.
Circumference of sphere of equal volume	24,901.42 mi.
Volume	236,680,000,000 cu. mi.
Surface area	196,950,000 sq. mi.
Land area	57,470,000 sq. mi.
Water area	139,480,000 sq. mi.
Mass	6.595 x 10^{21} tons
Density	344.7 lbs./cu. ft., or 5.522 gm/cc
Mean linear rotational velocity at equator	1040 m.p.h.
Mean linear speed in orbit	66,600 m.p.h.
Inclination (obliquity of ecliptic)	23.45°
Mean distance to moon	238,854 mi.
Mean distance to sun	92,900,000 mi.
Average depth of the oceans	12,000 to 13,000 ft. (very rough)
Average elevation of continents	
Europe	980 ft.
Australia	1000 ft.
South America	1800 ft.
Africa	1900 ft.
North America	2000 ft.
Asia	3000 ft.
Antarctica	6000 ft.
Maximum land elevation	29,003 ft.
Deepest ocean depth	35,700 ft.

Composite chemical composition of crust-ocean-atmosphere

Oxygen	46.4%	Iron	5.1%	Potassium	2.6%
Silicon	27.8%	Calcium	3.6%	Magnesium	2.1%
Aluminum	8.1%	Sodium	2.9%	All others	1.4%

CRUST ranges in thickness from 10 km* (counting water) under the oceans to 60 km under the continents. Has the average properties of granodiorite on continents, of basalt or gabbro under oceans. Temperatures may run from 0–1000°C.

MANTLE from Mohorovičić discontinuity down to 2900 km. The best guesses on composition are that it is made up of silicate rock, probably rich in iron and magnesium, in various physical states depending on temperature and pressure. Estimates of temperature range between 500–4200°C.

OUTER CORE: 2900–5100 km. This layer has a high density (11–12 gm/cc) and is called liquid since it does not appear to transmit shear waves. It may be quite a different sort of liquid from what we are accustomed to. Its composition has been called iron-nickel on the basis of meteorite studies and electrical properties, but it may be a high pressure phase of silicate rocks which make up the mantle.

INNER CORE: 5100–6370 km. This is also of high density and differs from the outer core in that it appears to be solid rather than liquid.

*1 km = .62 mi.

index

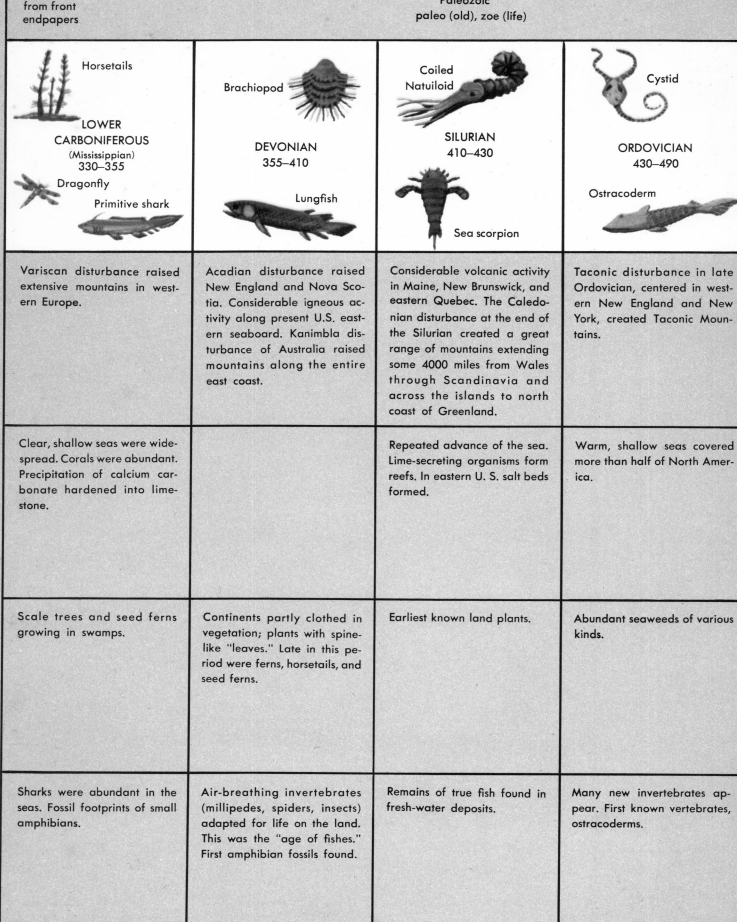

continued from front endpapers

Paleozoic
paleo (old), zoe (life)

LOWER CARBONIFEROUS (Mississippian) 330–355	DEVONIAN 355–410	SILURIAN 410–430	ORDOVICIAN 430–490
Horsetails / Dragonfly / Primitive shark	Brachiopod / Lungfish	Coiled Natuiloid / Sea scorpion	Cystid / Ostracoderm
Variscan disturbance raised extensive mountains in western Europe.	Acadian disturbance raised New England and Nova Scotia. Considerable igneous activity along present U.S. eastern seaboard. Kanimbla disturbance of Australia raised mountains along the entire east coast.	Considerable volcanic activity in Maine, New Brunswick, and eastern Quebec. The Caledonian disturbance at the end of the Silurian created a great range of mountains extending some 4000 miles from Wales through Scandinavia and across the islands to north coast of Greenland.	Taconic disturbance in late Ordovician, centered in western New England and New York, created Taconic Mountains.
Clear, shallow seas were widespread. Corals were abundant. Precipitation of calcium carbonate hardened into limestone.		Repeated advance of the sea. Lime-secreting organisms form reefs. In eastern U. S. salt beds formed.	Warm, shallow seas covered more than half of North America.
Scale trees and seed ferns growing in swamps.	Continents partly clothed in vegetation; plants with spine-like "leaves." Late in this period were ferns, horsetails, and seed ferns.	Earliest known land plants.	Abundant seaweeds of various kinds.
Sharks were abundant in the seas. Fossil footprints of small amphibians.	Air-breathing invertebrates (millipedes, spiders, insects) adapted for life on the land. This was the "age of fishes." First amphibian fossils found.	Remains of true fish found in fresh-water deposits.	Many new invertebrates appear. First known vertebrates, ostracoderms.